OUR NEXT FRONTIER

Other Books by Robert Rodale

The Basic Book of Organic Gardening
Sane Living in a Mad World
The Best Health Ideas I Know

OUR NEXT FRONTIER

A Personal Guide for Tomorrow's Lifestyle

by Robert Rodale

Rodale Press
Emmaus, Pennsylvania

Much of the text for this book
is based on material that
originally appeared in *Organic
Gardening* and *Prevention*
magazines, and some which
appeared in *Sane Living in a
Mad World* and *The Best
Health Ideas I Know.*

*Printed in the United States of America on recycled
paper, containing a high percentage of de-inked fiber.*

Book design by Darlene Schneck

Library of Congress Cataloging in Publication Data

Rodale, Robert.
    Our next frontier.

    Includes index.
    1. Food. 2. Diet. 3. Agriculture. I. Title.
TX353.R62   `   613   81-10649
ISBN 0-87857-365-8 hardcover AACR2
2 4 6 8 10 9 7 5 3 1 hardcover

Contents

Choosing Our Next Frontier

ᒪᒧ Those of you sitting on the left side of the plane can see the Grand Canyon below us."

It was the voice of the pilot on a flight from Los Angeles to Chicago. I had a left window seat, and I sat there enjoying a view of one of this country's finest spectacles.

Ten minutes passed, and the pilot switched on the plane's intercom again. This time he said something that got me upset.

"Look at all that empty land down there, with nobody living on it. Next time somebody tells you that this country is getting overpopulated, just think about that empty space. We have plenty of room for millions and millions more people."

Yes, I thought. There is space down there. And minerals too. But what about water? If you tried to build a city of a million or so people down there, what would the people drink? How would they flush their toilets?

And water is only one of the basic things we need to live happy and productive lives. We need fuel to change the temperature of our homes, and to be able to travel. We also need food, clothing, metals, plastics—literally hundreds of different raw materials that are processed and blended and shaped and assembled into goods.

Most of all, we need a frontier. By that I mean we need new territory to grow into, as our numbers grow. Yes, the pilot was right in understanding that need. Even here in America, despite access to birth control methods, our population grows at the rate of five thousand people a day. And some level of population growth—perhaps not quite that great—is likely to continue well into our future.

The thought that we don't have the space or the resources to provide a good way of life for more people comes hard to us. America is the land of the greatest, most fertile, most productive frontier ever opened. For almost five hundred years our lands have absorbed and sheltered millions of immigrants from Europe, Africa, and Asia. The new people used the new land to build a nation richer than any the world has ever seen. That transformation of raw plains and mountains into a great country is clearly understood by all, and the history of that change is the foundation of our cultural heritage.

What is less clearly understood is that our first frontier came to an absolute end about one hundred years ago. The original American frontier was raw land, occupied "only" by Indians and wild animals, both of whom could be pushed aside. Yes, there are still unoccupied spaces in this country, as that pilot saw from his 35,000-foot vantage point, but they are not empty in the frontier sense. These vast open spaces hold resources that we cannot see until they are literally brought to the surface. And it was the realization that we had the means to exploit these resources that opened up our second frontier.

Looking for more resources to expand our economy, we began digging down into a fossil bonanza beneath our feet—pumping up oil, digging out coal, mining iron and other minerals. Those riches had been stored away in the earth by nature for millions of years and were waiting for our use just the way the land of the new continent stretched before the eyes of early settlers. And like those apparently endless prairies and forests and mountain ranges that stretched before us, the fossil resources also looked limitless.

For many years we used the resources of the second frontier to increase the value of the first. Fossil energy and mined minerals were converted into fertilizers, pesticides, machines, and services to boost the yield of our farms. And we built cars and trucks by the millions each year, to move ourselves and our goods where needed. Agriculture and transport are just two of the different sectors of our economy that benefited from the exploitation of the two frontiers. Although America consists of only a small fraction of the world's population, we have created a supernation using fully a third of all the world's energy and goods.

Now, we are beginning to see that the second frontier will someday come to an end, too. That is a new experience for us. We should have known back in the 1800s that if you plow a long enough furrow, eventually you'll reach another ocean. When we tapped into that first oil well, we should have sensed—and begun to think about—a time when the oil would be used up. Right now we are digging coal out of the earth, thinking that there remain hundreds of years' worth of the black fuel. We keep on digging, seeking fuel for a way of life that is based on a frontier that is draining away underneath us. It is taking a long time to expire, but that won't change things. The end is bound to come.

Where do we go from here?

There are those who look beyond earth, to outer space, for our next frontier. They envision a switch from the exploitation of underground space to the exploration and settlement of space colonies. Impressed with the apparent ease and speed with which people reached the moon, they see the vast reaches of space as a frontier that can be shaped into a series of homelands for our expanding population. But while other planets may indeed hold treasures that can enrich and preserve our future, it will likely be many decades before we here on earth can venture into that far-off territory.

We should not be deceived by the successes of our past space missions. Those efforts used up tremendous amounts of nonrenewable natural resources. The fuel and minerals that would be needed to power more ambitious explorations as well as construction in other parts of our solar system would be so great as to be virtually incomprehensible. And to survive in the hostile environment of outer space calls for continuous support. The air, moisture, and complex range of life systems needed to support the human organism are, to the best of our knowledge, available only here. The creation of an entirely new biosphere may not be beyond the creative capability of human brain and could even be within the power of the human hand. But could the resources of earth's second frontier stand that extra strain?

I believe our next frontier is right here on earth, and it is a frontier already at hand.

This third frontier will be shaped by our ability to stand our ground, to face up to the end of the era of oil, to save what farmland we have left, to reduce the use of the water that cannot be replaced, and, most importantly, to make better use of the renewable resources whose great potential we are just now beginning to realize. We will have to use all the insight and skill within our power to make this renewable resources frontier last—until we're ready for the next one.

As dramatic as this all sounds, we should not by any means see this new frontier as one of desperation or limited options. Rather, it can be a time of many opportunities and a chance to enhance the quality of our lives and our environment.

Consider, for a moment, how little renewable resources have been explored so far. Our efforts to use the current rays of the sun for power, instead of tapping into deposits of sun-created fossil fuels, have just begun. Our formidable scientific resources have barely been applied at all to the challenge of helping the land produce food in a permanent way, or to people-powered transportation, or to making the best use of our precious water supplies. Only now are we starting to think of ways to put our abundant mineral and organic wastes to work, instead of letting them accumulate and become burdens. Couldn't we put *renewable* resources to better use too, using them in hundreds or even thousands of both old and new ways to create the means to improve our lives?

Wouldn't the challenge of doing that give a new sense of purpose to our lives, and even help to restore our control of how we live? The more we rely on oil and other nonrenewable resources, the more our lives (and eventually even our thinking) fall under the sway of the people and organizations controlling those deposits. We need to find many different ways to escape that trap.

Many people have already begun to live lives focused on the exploitation of this third frontier. They have decided that they want to live more in tune with nature, making the most appropriate use of earth's gifts, and, most of all, creating maximum health for themselves so they will have the strength to help build a new kind of future. I know that people who have freely and consciously adopted this lifestyle, are, as a group, more well adjusted to their environment and more satisfied with the material things they have than are people who live without the benefit of a philosophy of real environmental and resource consciousness, or self-reliance, as many call it.

Their number grows continually, as does their influence on the decisions and lifestyles of others. Collectively, they are beginning to have an impact on the way society as a whole perceives its options for future direction. The average person today—early 1981—has yet to feel that either the sun or renewable energy can heat all homes. But that same person knows that some homes are heated that way, and that the onward march of technology and the pressures of economic realities are making solar heating more of a mainstream option with each passing year.

In the same way, gardens and small farms are becoming more important as sources of fresh foods. Ways are being found to avoid insect damage without the use of toxic pesticides. And the creation of health is moving out of the province of the physician (where as an idea it rested uneasily for only a few decades), back to the mind and body of the person who can both improve and enjoy that health.

A major purpose of this book is to suggest the necessity for exploiting this third frontier, and also to convince you that it is, in fact, a frontier, one critical to our personal and our planet's well-being, maybe even survival. It is a frontier that will ready us and bide us time for, perhaps, another frontier that will take us beyond the limits of earth.

There are many ways to stand our ground, to use the land and the renewable resources that are all around us, and still be able to build a better way of life for more people. To do that we will have to use less of some things and more of others. The land, the sun, the wind, and the rain will have to be used more diligently and creatively. And we must be more cautious and careful in our use of oil, minerals, coal, gas, and other resources that do, in fact, have and end.

I start this book with an explanation of the great promise of gardening as a way to venture into the third frontier. I take that route because gardening is the most convenient point of entry to the idea of self-reliance. There is land all around us that can be gardened, even within our greatest cities. And we can manage to garden in a totally biological way, using only our minds, our muscle power, and renewable resources to create the finest quality food in abundance.

So start your venture into the future by stepping into a garden—at least figuratively. But be prepared to go further. This is by no means a book just about gardens. The third frontier is everywhere.

1 THE ORGANIC GARDENING IDEA

The Organic Gardening Idea

onservation and natural living may be a vital necessity in the decade of the 80s—a life preserver within reach of people drowning in the effluence of their own mistakes. The virgin land is no more. The quiet places in the country are being built up. Air and water are dirty almost everywhere.

Under today's conditions it's easy to see the reward of being and thinking like an organic gardener. What could be more valuable now than a small garden, free of synthetic fertilizers and pesticides, yielding food that tastes as good as the vegetables and fruits we used to be able to buy in markets years ago? Valuable not only to the body but also to the spirit.

Even before the full flowering of the chemical age, though, the organic gardening idea was a full-grown philosophy. In fact, the pollution and degradation which so many people experience today were predicted almost fifty years ago by the founders of the organic method. They could see evidence then of trouble and felt that the growing use of artificial fertilizers and pesticide chemicals would eventually spread a pall of illness throughout society. The organic gardening idea goes back a long way. Even more significantly, organic gardening as an idea goes far into the future, projecting the possiblity of a pleasant and rewarding way of life in an increasingly synthetic world.

Organic thinking began with Sir Albert Howard, an English agricultural advisor to the Indian state of Indore in the 1920s and 1930s. Howard saw that India had no money to buy synthetic chemicals, yet its population was growing and it needed more food. So he began to develop farming systems based entirely on renewable resources. Howard devised ways to recycle the nutrients available locally—animal manure and leftover plant materials.

In what became known as the Indore method of composting, he taught farmers to layer rough weeds and crop wastes with high-nitrogen manure and a little soil, making a pile that soon heated up to over 150° Fahrenheit (66° Celsius) as a result of bacterial action. Lacking machinery and power, the native farmers had no mechanical means to deal with those "wastes." By composting, however, they were able to break down stalks and leaves and to create a valuable soil conditioner and fertilizer which could replace the nutrients and humus removed from the soil by crops.

There was more to Howard's thinking than just finding a solution to an immediate practical problem, however. He was disturbed by the scientific community's advocacy of synthetic substitutes for many natural commodities, a stance based on the discoveries of the nineteenth century German chemist, Justus von Liebig. Hailed as a pioneer of a new age of science, von Liebig had demonstrated the chemical simplicity of plant matter simply by burning it and analyzing the ash. He found nitrogen (N), phosphorus (P), and potash (K), but ignored the organic portion of the plant. The chemical fertilizer industry grew from the ash of von Liebig's experiment. Salesmen told farmers that N, P, and K were all that mattered in the soil, and that replacing them in powder form could assure fertility indefinitely. As we know, the chemical fertilizer message spread around the world quite effectively, and became the foundation of today's industrialized agriculture.

Howard rightly perceived in von Liebig's doctrine something extremely dangerous—the rupture of the cycle of life. Under the "scientific" system of farming, soil became primarily something to hold up plants so they could be fed with artificial solutions. The age-old rhythms of nature which had built the soil were violated. Howard began preaching that it was possible for thinking farmers to preserve the cycle of life by returning plant and animal wastes to the soil, by countering insects by nonpoisonous means, and by avoiding the synthetic, soluble fertilizers with their toxic residues. If the cycle of life wasn't preserved, said Howard, future generations would be faced with declining fertility, hunger, and increases in disease and pollution.

My father, J. I. Rodale, first read about Sir Albert Howard's ideas in the late 1930s. Even then, the United States was so industrialized and technologically "advanced" that it was possible to see that what Howard was predicting could easily occur. The American Dust Bowl experience of the Depression years was graphic evidence of the disruption of the cycle of life. But there were signs of trouble everywhere. Food quality was low. Pollution was intruding on people's lives. Disease caused by physical degeneration—not just by microbes—was increasing. J. I. noted with dismay that the grim harvest predicted was about to be reaped.

My father first used the word *organic* to describe the natural method of gardening and farming, mainly because compost, humus, and the organic fraction of the soil were emphasized so strongly. However, even in 1942, J. I. saw that this method was more than just a way to husband the soil and grow plants and animals. He proclaimed that to be "organic" was to know, to understand, and to use the lessons of nature in the evaluation of the "blessings" of science and technology. What good was it, he asked, to grow food without using chemical fertilizers or pesticides, if it were then processed and its content of vitamins and minerals seriously depleted? In fact, not caring whether he was called an extremist or a crackpot, J. I. created what might now be called a "strict constructionist" interpretation of natural life under the banner of organiculture. If it is synthetic, avoid it, he said. If it goes through a factory, examine it with special care. Follow the dictates of the cycle of life when growing things, he advised, and you will be blessed with foods of surprising taste and quality that are little troubled by insects or disease.

J. I. demonstrated the value of these ideas by creating a research farm based on Howard's concept just outside Emmaus,

Pennsylvania. "We will farm using only manure and wasted organic matter as fertilizer, and won't use poisonous pesticides," he said to himself. Then he expanded the concept of his organic research. "We will look also for ways to improve the health of people by growing better food." A visitor coming to J. I. Rodale's farm would see fine crops of grain, healthy animals, and productive gardens. Underlying all, however, was an effort to achieve a much bigger harvest—a better way of life based on natural principles.

In recent years, events have forced the concept underlying organic research to expand even further. There is an energy crisis, and the nonorganic way of growing food uses too much energy. Our environment has become contaminated by agricultural chemicals, many of which pollute the normal sources of food. The ozone layer of the upper atmosphere, which screen harmful rays of the sun, is threatened with destruction by the overuse of chemical nitrogen fertilizers. Inflation has forced the cost of food to new highs, and the food-distribution web has become so complex that economic or military disruption could cause widespread suffering. Because of these and similar conditions, there is now a need for a concept of organic research that will support an effort going far beyond the basic goals of natural soil improvement and improved food quality. To meet the challenge, those of us continuing J. I.'s work are involved in a major research effort at a second site. The Organic Gardening and Farming Research Center is located on a 305-acre farm near Maxatawny, Pennsylvania. All the experiments being done there are aimed at finding out how to do more with less—how to make organic methods even more efficient than they are already.

Although there is now wide acceptance of organic methods, that wasn't true in the early days—during the 40s and 50s. We were accused of not living in the twentieth century. Humus in the soil is important, the opponents said, but there isn't enough compost to go around. Almost everyone agreed that old-fashioned, natural agriculture produced tastier foods, but few would admit it was possible to grow them now on a large scale.

The happenings of the past few years have changed a lot of minds. Many can now see the direct result of the misuse of our environment and of the failure of industry and agriculture to adapt to constraints of the cycle of life. You no longer need be a prophet or a visionary to perceive that abuse of our world is leading to trouble. Of course, there is still opposition to the organic method. Those who depend on continuing chemical doctoring of land, water, and air tend to refuse to believe that only natural ways can lead to a better and more pure world. There are still people who say that the now-banned DDT is needed. There are still strong voices raised in favor of burning garbage, because composting it might cost more.

I know—and I think you do, too—that the organic way of living points to the right road, even though that road might have a few bumps and hills in it. The organic idea is a plan for positive action. In a world increasingly beset by negative influences, there is more need than ever for a positive approach. And there couldn't be a better place to start than with the soil beneath our feet. Growing food naturally, using renewable resources, provides the basic foundation for the building of a livable society.

The Plant World

In coming years, those of us concerned about the environment likely will spend more time worrying about green plants than about factory smokestacks and chemical dumpsites. For the plant world is an absolutely vital link in our ecological system. Even if someday we succeed in solving the newsworthy problems of pollution, we will still be lost unless we can build up and maintain the regenerative powers of the green plant world.

The more we study, the more we see that plants are indispensable. They are the foundation of our life-support system, for they are the strongest force in moderating the tendencies of nature to pollute itself. Without plants, the earth would be as barren as the moon. With plants, it is a comfortable home for man. Furthermore, plants are a buffer between man and the earth, feeding us and preventing us from destroying the quality of our environment. But plants will do these things only if we make sure that there are enough of them, and that they are healthy.

There are many ways plants help improve our environment and make living on this planet possible for human beings.

1. Plants build topsoil. When our earth was formed, the only things present were rock, fire, water, and gas. There was no soil, and especially no topsoil—that fragile and extremely thin layer of life-producing substance. Primitive forms of plants—similar to the lichens—began to grow on rocks and in crevices at an early period in history, and gradually refined the dust ground from rocks into humus-rich topsoil. The process of topsoil-building is still going on, wherever healthy green plants are growing.

2. Plants control erosion. Man has accelerated the process of erosion by water and wind through bad farming and grazing practices, but soil was destroyed before he came on the scene. Only where green plants are growing is the soil anchored firmly to the earth, and even then erosion is not prevented completely.

Many American rivers run muddy after a rain, and some are muddy all the time. We can do a great deal to stop the degradation of our environment and the disruption of its ecological balance by restoring green plant life to those barren soils now silting running waters.

After the Dust Bowl experience of the 30s the conservation movement gained great popular acceptance because of its program to prevent erosion. For a few decades, the soil and its plant cover were the focus of attention of the conservation movement. Now that nuclear and chemical threats and shortages of energy preoccupy us, people are thinking less about the needs of the soil. Maybe it is time to lower our eyes and take another look at the plants keeping us alive.

3. Plants convert carbon dioxide to oxygen. Every time we burn something, oxygen from the air is consumed, and carbon dioxide is produced. Without some means to convert that carbon dioxide back into oxygen, we would all soon choke to death. Fortunately, plants have the ability to turn carbon dioxide into

oxygen through the process of photosynthesis. Only green plants have that ability.

Nevertheless, we are in trouble. The rate of our burning exceeds the capacity of the world's plants to complete the oxygen cycle. The United States alone consumes over 30 percent of the world's energy. And most of that energy comes from the combustion of oil and coal. Our dependence on these fossil fuels is not only increasing the likelihood of global war but is endangering the biosphere, for the intense fires they produce are consuming oxygen at a rapid rate. And while luxuriating in the power of coal and oil, we have allowed our plant resources to be depleted. Forests have been cut down on all the major continents. Highways, homes, factories, and public buildings have been erected on land that formerly supported plant life. Even the oceans' vast stores of oxygen-producing plant life are threatened by creeping pollution. There is a possibility that our climate has already been altered by carbon dioxide excesses in the air.

4. Plants are essential to our supply of water. Both trees and smaller green plants create a good environment for rainwater to soak into the soil, feeding vital underground streams. Rain hitting a bare slope would soon pound the soil surface into an impenetrable hardpan. Plants slow the velocity of falling rain, and with their roots, make many fine channels for that moisture to enter the soil.

Wherever man reduces plant life by improper farming practices or excessive building, the water supply suffers. There is no need to reemphasize the importance to health and well-being of ample water supplies.

5. Plants control temperature. Walk into a forest on a hot day and you'll immediately notice a drop in temperature. The shade of the leaves breaks the rays of the sun, and moisture being released by the trees helps to cool the air.

Trees and plants are also effective windbreaks. In some exposed and windy places, farming and even pleasant living depend entirely on the protection afforded by windbreaks of trees.

6. Plants are essential to the recycling of human and animal wastes. For a long time, people thought sewage plants provided the ultimate disposal for human wastes. Now we are finding that

such mechanical and biological treatment of excrement is not completely acceptable. Sludge remains, which must be recycled back to the land and consumed by plants to complete the life cycle. Even the water released by sewage plants—though it appears clear and odorless—is rich in nitrogen, phosphorus, and other nutrients that can cause the excessive growth of algae in lakes and rivers. Algae consume all the oxygen in water and choke out other forms of life there. The only completely effective treatment for sewage water is to spray it on the land, where plants can use the nutrients effectively.

Any farmer or gardener who has ever spread manure on the land knows how obvious and effective that technique is. In only a few weeks, it soaks into the earth, to be converted by microbes into food for plants. There is no better way, except for the intermediate process of composting, to handle manure. Lately, farmers have begun to congregate their animals in pens (as people are crowded into cities) and are now facing the same troubles confronting those responsible for treating city sewage wastes. Instead of being used to feed plants, the manure residues from those feedlots drain unused into rivers and lakes, causing excessive algae growth and other problems.

Or they are allowed to accumulate in foul-smelling open ponds called lagoons. Often, such ponds cause complaints, and sometimes lawsuits, by homeowners buying land near intensive animal-feeding operations. As a result of this friction, some farms have been closed. The public relations problem is getting so bad that farmers are being forced to defend their livelihood by supporting right-to-farm ordinances. In some states such bills are being considered by the legislatures.

If the present exodus from major cities into surrounding farmland continues, more and more country dwellers will be kept awake nights by the stench of ever-more-concentrated farming practices. This sad situation dramatizes the unavoidable truth of my statement that unless plants are used to recycle human and animal wastes, we will not have an effective means of preserving the quality of our environment.

7. Plants are an economical source of nutrients. Though that statement is obviously true, you might question its relevance

to environmental quality. I include it to draw a contrast between the economy of plants as food and the expense of meat and even milk. We are creating environmental problems for ourselves by overconsumption of animal products. Animals, like human beings, are sometimes wasteful in their use of food. It takes 21.4 pounds of plant protein to yield one pound of beef protein. By featuring meat as a central part of our diet, we make inefficient use of our resources. Meat in very moderate amounts is healthy, but to the extent eaten by Americans it can cause obesity and possible heart disease. So it would be far better for our health as well as our environment if we ourselves ate more of the corn, barley, oats, and soybeans grown in this country instead of feeding such good sources of vegetable protein mostly to livestock as we do now.

8. Plants are indicators of pollution. Tobacco, that black sheep of the plant world, may yet find an affectionate place in our hearts. It is responsive to minute changes in the quality of air, detectable by no other practical means. Experts can measure air pollution by studying tobacco growth in certain areas. Another plant that can monitor environmental changes is the spiderwort. Certain strains of this commonplace little plant can accurately indicate increases in radiation by changing color.

Other plants and trees also serve as indicators of environmental damage, even though they are not as sensitive as tobacco or spiderwort. In some areas of the western United States, forests around refineries and smelters have been killed or stunted. Plants growing near busy traffic have been found to have a high lead content, a residue of the automobile exhaust sprayed on them. That finding has brought into serious question the practice of growing commercial or garden crops near heavily traveled streets or highways.

9. Plants are a rich storehouse of chemical information. They harbor within themselves a tremendous chemical imagination, and each different type is made up of its own panorama of compounds. These chemicals, found in plants in such rich profusion, are not only the ordinary types—the kinds you would find in bottles on the shelves of a druggist or in a school chemistry laboratory. Many of them are so diverse, and so unusual in their

function, that even to this day plant chemicals are seen by scientists as a treasure trove of inspiration. The leaves of unusual plants are still being analyzed to see whether the chemicals they contain might be useful as new drugs or as pesticides, or to suggest solutions to any one of dozens of chemical problems.

Why have plants spawned so many different chemical compounds? I think there can be only one reason. They do it to survive (which in turn helps us to live better).

Think about the challenge of plant survival for a moment. There are tens of thousands of different types of plants on this earth. They live under all different kinds of climatic and soil conditions. Some nestle among rocks on mountainsides, and others find their niche in swamps or in humid jungles. Everywhere there are differences in the kind of soil, in the diseases and insects that cause trouble, and in the community of other plants in which plants live. No wonder that for survival plants have created such a rich storehouse for inner diversity. Keep in mind also that plants can't move around the way animals, birds, and insects do, so they reflect more closely the unique chemical makeup of the place where they live. Soils are remarkably different from one place to another, so to some extent plants merely mirror that diversity in the elements they feed from.

Primitive peoples learned to use the chemical diversity of plants in many ways, but primarily to preserve their health. Thousands of years ago, people who knew nothing of chemistry identified those plants which contained basic drugs like quinine, curare, caffeine, and many others which are still in use today. They knew which plants were rich sources of vitamins, and sought them out. In primitive societies—as in many Third World countries today—human survival depended to a great extent on knowing how to put to use the chemicals in local plants.

Today, we don't absolutely have to know plant chemistry to survive. If we want, we can go to a drugstore or a doctor and get synthetic medicines (although some are actually synthetic imitations of chemical ideas that came from plants originally). But people are going back to plant medicine anyway, because they see it as a way to increase their wellness. Herbalism is a fast-growing art. Herb gardens are sprouting up everywhere, herb teas are selling faster than ever, books on herb culture are extremely popular, and herbs are rapidly gaining popularity for use as food flavors. The natural chemical diversity present in plants is also being understood better as we explore "new" ways to garden that are in reality old ways that are again being seen as very sensible and useful. (I am referring mainly to companion planting and interplanting, which are efforts to create in our gardens communities that allow plants to grow in more comfortable and efficient ways.)

10. People are happier when looking at plants. I saved for last this extremely important way plants help to improve our environment. Pollution touches the soul as well as the body. We have been born of the soil and are supported by the products of the soil, and there is something within each of us which cannot forget the great meaning that plants give to life.

A city with perfectly pure air and water and with an absence of crime would still be inhospitable without trees or vegetation. One of the greatest frustrations for New Yorkers is that their parks have become unsafe in the evenings. The same could be said of other cities. We can relax more easily and completely under a tree than on the finest sofa.

A Gallup Poll reported in the *New York Times* revealed that "six of 10 adults living in the nation's metropolitan centers would move to less urbanized areas if they could live anywhere they wished." Over fifteen hundred adults were interviewed. Only 18 percent said they would like to continue living in a city. Twenty-six percent said they preferred the suburbs, and 31 percent chose a small town as the best place to live. Twenty-four percent said farm life appealed to them, while only 1 percent had no opinion. One of the most obvious features of farm and small town life is the opportunity it offers of associating with the plant world. Apparently no city today can offer features that the average person values more highly.

Putting Plant Disease in Its Proper Ecological Perspective

W ise people know that the world would be an unhealthy place if we didn't have disease. If science could find cures for all diseases, it would immediately have to invent new ones. Without illness, the world would soon be smothered in unwanted plant, human, and animal life. The helping hand of disease is a vital factor in shaping the forms of life.

In his enduring book, A *Sand County Almanac*, Aldo Leopold made a pungent and accurate observation about the value of plant disease:

> *Every farm woodland, in addition to yielding lumber, fuel, and posts, should provide its owner a liberal education. This crop of wisdom never fails, but it is not always harvested. . . . Soon after I bought the woods a decade ago, I realized that I had bought almost as many tree diseases as I had trees. My woodlot is riddled by all the ailments wood is heir to. I began to wish that Noah, when he loaded up the Ark, had left the trees behind. But it soon became clear that these same diseases made my woodlot a mighty fortress, unequaled in the whole country.*

Ecologically, Leopold said, tree disease built strength into the whole natural population of his woods. Coons thrived on his farm because a maple tree, weakened and ultimately uprooted by fungus disease, provided at its base a snug harbor during hunting season. Ruffed grouse were numerous because they ate the galls of the oak leaves, caused when the tender new twigs are stung by a gall wasp. Wild bees loaded up the innards of diseased, hollow oaks with honey. Rabbits ate the bark of his dogwoods, but only after it became infested with oyster shell scale. A flock of a dozen chickadees spent the winter in his woods. When Leopold cut the dead trees for firewood, the "chicks," as he called them, hastened to dine on the "treasure of eggs, larvae and cocoons" under each slab of dead bark. A prothonotary warbler was the "real jewel" of Leopold's woods, living in an old woodpecker hole. "The flash of his gold-and-blue plumage amid the dank decay of the Hune woods is in itself proof that dead trees are transmuted into living animals, and vice versa."

Many nonorganic gardeners and farmers have had trouble seeing disease and insect problems in their true, ecological perspective. They view their gardens and farms as factories for the production of food or as displays of the clean, undiseased kind of beauty which their limited education has allowed them to appreciate. Any intruder—be it a disease, an insect, or a foraging bird—is automatically classed as an enemy, and its demise is fervently desired. They spray with poisons to kill these pests, thereby tainting the food they produce and killing their chance of witnessing the kind of spectacular natural display Leopold described. The pests, unfortunately, usually survive the poisoning.

Your first step in having the right attitude toward disease and insects is to avoid hysteria. You can't learn all the important natural lessons at once, but you can quickly grasp the necessity for learning, and you can exercise your powers of observation, which are the key to success in translating natural evidence into understandable signals.

When disease strikes in your garden, don't ask, "Why did this have to happen to me?" Rather, ask yourself, "What am I doing that is out of step with nature's scheme for this area?"

New gardeners frequently make the mistake of planting what they like to eat, rather than what they believe will grow healthfully in their area. Old gardeners have learned what nature will allow them to do successfully where they live, and they tend to operate their gardens with more ecological sense. They have learned the hard way.

Sometimes we are very resistant to nature's educational process, however. It happens most often with fruit growing, I believe. Almost universally, we have the American dream of a house with some land and an orchard. We don't demand high productivity, but we do want variety. We want peaches, apples, pears, raspberries, strawberries, plums, cherries, grapes, walnuts, and perhaps a chestnut or two, and of course we want two or three varieties of each. Just about every area is well suited for growing some kind of fruit, but I don't think there is any place a commercial grower would try to grow the variety the average home gardener wants. Can you succeed where a commercial grower would be likely to fail?

If you try to grow every fruit you like to eat, the chances are good that nature will put its disease force to work on a good portion of your selection, simply because climate or soil or moisture conditions where you live are not really good for every plant. I'm not suggesting you stop trying to grow a variety of fruits in your garden. But I do think the sensible thing to do is to concentrate your efforts on those plants you know are most likely to thrive. Grow the others, too, but in lesser quantity, and be sure not to spray bugs for the sake of a plant that may well be out of place in your garden.

Even farmers have much to learn about plant placement and variety. We could grow, I am sure, all the food we need without using any poisonous sprays, if Americans would farm on a sensible ecological basis. Nature uses disease and insects to tell us that some plants grow better in some parts of our country than in others. Disease and insects demonstrate that apples grow better in some parts of Virginia than they do in Pennsylvania. There are many such signals given to us by nature, but many people ignore them. Farmers grow what they do for economic rather than ecological reasons. And they use the myriad of chemical pesticides available to try to make economic sense out of their ecological mistakes. Chemical farming is a form of warfare against nature, and we should have learned by now that nobody really wins wars.

Organic gardeners usually take a position somewhere between the live-and-let-live philosophy of Aldo Leopold and the chemical warfare approach. They build up their soil so it will be healthy and productive, expecting that health to impart to their plants an excellent chance of outpacing natural enemies. Local resources like leaves, garbage, sawdust, and manure are used for soil building. So are natural minerals such as ground phosphate rock, limestone, and materials rich in potash. This natural approach alerts us to the unrecognized value of wastes around us and prevents the chemical overkill that works against fertility and opens the door to disease.

The average chemically treated soil has what you might describe as acid indigestion or heartburn. So much "rich food" in the way of superphosphate, soluble nitrates, muriate of potash, and other synthetic goodies has been poured into it that its system of digestion has been altered. Natural soil is full of microorganisms—bacteria, fungi, molds, and so forth—which play an extremely important role in constantly renewing its fertility. They convert leaves, stalks of plants, and any other rough organic materials that come their way into nutrients that are readily available to the roots of plants, to use as food. This "soil life," as it is sometimes called, works for nothing. It is both free and very effective. With little work on the part of the gardener or farmer, these tiny plants and animals regenerate the land.

When large amounts of artificial fertilizers are applied, the small-scale soil life diminishes. Valuable small animals like earthworms are killed outright by strongly acid fertilizers. Weed killers and pesticides don't help them either. And the loss is a great one because preliminary research has revealed that certain vigorous species of earthworms have the ability to make available to plants needed minerals that are present in the soil in locked-up form. That beneficial effect was reported with calcium, magnesium, phosphorus, and molybdenum. In other words, if the worms in the soil are encouraged to grow by not poisoning them with chemical fertilizers and pesticides and by supplying them raw organic matter to use as food, they'll pay you back by helping your plants take from the soil the minerals they need.

Years ago an extremely exciting study by Henry Hopp and Clarence S. Slater of the U.S. Department of Agriculture revealed that earthworms produce a natural plant-growth stimulant that makes plants grow better in some way that we don't understand completely. In careful pot experiments, plants were grown in wormless soil and in soil to which dead and live earthworms were added. The dead worms helped to fertilize the soil with the nutrients in their bodies, but the live worms did a far better job. "Beneficial chemicals" were released by the worms, said Hopp and Slater.

Earthworms aside, chemical fertilizers also lower the population of other soil organisms, in part because there is less need for their services. When large amounts of chemical nitrogen are pumped into the soil, natural nitrogen-producing organisms like the *Azotobacter* (which take nitrogen from the air) don't multiply as rapidly. Why should they? There is little need for their services.

Organic gardeners, though, create conditions that allow such nitrogen producers in their soil to thrive and multiply. Another way of doing this is to use bacterial "fertilizers."

I put that word in quotes, because cultures of these bacteria don't actually contain much nitrogen. But putting concentrated quantities of such bacteria in the soil boosts the capacity of the land to capture more nitrogen from the air. Much of the work on these natural aids to fertility has been done in India, where the nitrogen situation is critical.

At Tamil Nadu Agricultural University, scientists found that by dipping seedlings of rice, ragi (*Eleusine coracana*), and tomato in *Azotobacter* cultures, growth has been significantly improved. The need for chemical fertilizer nitrogen has been cut in half—yet yields stay the same. And merely treating seeds of those plants with efficient strains of *Azotobacter* "has been found to enhance seedling growth by about 10 to 20 percent, and improve crop stand in the field." I am quoting from an article on bacterial fertilizers by G. Rangaswami, Ph.D., formerly the vice chancellor of Tamil Nadu Agricultural University.

The implications of this work for organic gardeners and farmers are enormous. Treating seeds and seedlings with *Azotobacter* strains specially bred for improved performance will enable you to get improved yields without paying any chemical company for nitrogen. You will be helping your soil and plants capture more of the free nitrogen from the air. That is a totally natural and organic technique. All you are doing is improving the efficiency and effectiveness of the bacterial nitrogen "manufacturing" that normally goes on in the soil.

Blue-green algae are also being cultured in India in a different effort to capture air nitrogen. These remarkable organisms thrive in warm climates on marshy ground, such as in moist rice paddies between crops. You've probably seen blue-green algae growing on the ground many times, but didn't know that it was effectively capturing nitrogen from the air.

Because the cost of nitrogen fertilizer is so high, there is a good possibility that blue-green algae can be grown commercially and applied to the soil as a natural organic fertilizer—at a cost which may someday be even lower than the cost of chemical nitrogen.

Think of the implications of this exciting field of research! If present oil and fertilizer price trends continue, natural and organic ways of capturing nitrogen from the air could become cheaper than the cost of chemical nitrogen. Actually, natural methods are cheaper now for those farmers and gardeners willing to structure their growing systems to encourage nitrogen-fixing organisms. That is done by building the humus content of the soil, rotating crops, and avoiding the use of chemicals that reduce populations of soil organisms.

In addition to encouraging the kind of soil life that builds fertility, organic gardeners also counter disease by using natural means to tip the balance of productivity in their favor. They can do that by growing a large variety of plants and using disease-resistant varieties.

America's farmers have learned to their sorrow that monoculture can create vulnerability to disease. In breeding a corn plant suited to industrialized agriculture, scientists compromised disease resistance. When blight attacked the almost endless fields of corn in our heartland, there was almost no natural resistance. If crops had been rotated and if corn had not been genetically manipulated, the blight might have stayed within a limited area. Perhaps it would never have become a problem at all.

It's instructive to compare that disaster with the diversification used in India, where a wide variety of grains and other staple crops are grown on very small plots averaging five acres, with tools and machinery quite similar to those used by America's gardeners.

Yes, to create true food security we need to grow a wider variety of crops, for somehow, in still mysterious ways, plants of different species and types draw strength from each other, generating a subtle pattern of chemical interactions for their own protection. And it would be well for some of the plants we grow to be older strains, which have a greater natural resistance to disease and insect damage than many of the higher-yielding new cultivars.

One final and very important point. Disease is not caused by viruses and bacteria. When bacteria and other microorganisms were discovered a century or so ago, and when their important relationship to disease was perceived, it was concluded that these minute things were the cause of the disease. We now know that they are not the cause, but the *agents* of disease.

If disease is truly caused by microorganisms, everyone would be diseased, because viruses and bacteria are everywhere. The truth is that a host of factors usually combine to unhinge the normal defense mechanisms and allow disease to get a foothold. Even in the worst epidemics, not everyone gets sick. Not even all those who lack immunity will automatically get sick.

In his book, *Human Ecology and Health*, Dr. E. S. Rogers of the University of California said that ". . . illness is rarely the result of the impact of a single discrete, disease-causing agent (such as the tubercle bacillus). . . . Rather . . . most illness is an expression of a basic imbalance in man's physiological adaptation." There is almost never a single cause of disease. An organism has to get out of adjustment with its environment in a variety of ways for disease to occur.

The organic method gives plants better protection against disease than the standard methods of prevention or cure. We are seeking balance and wholeness, and a proper place for ourselves, our plants, and our animals in nature. Not an exclusive place, but a proper place. There will always be some disease. There always should be some disease. But if we listen for the signals that nature gives us and use that information to build strength naturally, plants will be as healthy as they deserve to be. Can we ask for anything more?

Living with Insects

The modern farmer's dream of being able to lick his insect enemies with super-powerful poisons has turned into a nightmare. We have weapons that are every bit as deadly to insects as the H-bomb is to human beings, yet we are losing the war against bugs. The more we spray with malathion, sevin, diazinon, and their chemical relatives, the more numerous the insects seem to get, and like automobiles, they come out every year in new, improved models.

A more natural approach to insect control *must* serve us better in the long run than one that poisons our environment while failing to subdue the bugs we see as enemies. A good place to start is with the realization that sometimes insects that chew or suck on plants don't cause damage. In fact, miracle of miracles, insect attack can actually be beneficial to plants.

Here are some examples, from experimental reports and observations by scientists:

Cucumbers infested by mites for up to eleven weeks yielded more than "clean" plants. (But if the infestation lasted more than fifteen weeks, yields decreased.)

Wheat kept free of aphids yielded almost a bushel less per acre than wheat that was being attacked by up to 200 aphids per linear foot.

Cotton and potatoes show similar effects. When a certain amount of cotton flowers or potato leaves were removed by insects, yields increased.

"Light browsing" of shrubs by insects (removing 65 to 70 percent of current growth) was found to have invigorating effects. When insects were kept away in later years, the shrubs suffered.

Field beans sometimes do better when there are small colonies of aphids on the plants during the first three weeks of growth.

Turnips also sometimes thrive better with moderate insect attack.

All of the above instances of plants being helped by insect attack are reported in the scientific literature. They are summarized in a fascinating article in the journal *Agro-Ecosystems* by P. Harris of the Agriculture Canada Research Station in Regina, Saskatchewan. The title of his paper is "A Possible Explanation of Plant Yield Increases Following Insect Damage."

Harris offers two possible explanations for these remarkable effects.

First, early-season insect attack sometimes causes plants to send out more shoots or "tillers." Some grains are programmed by their evolution to send only one shoot as high as possible, reaching for more light in a crowd of other plants. Even when grown with plenty of space, they retain that upward-reaching habit. Early-season insect attack prunes those plants effectively, causing them to send out more shoots. Those extra shoots form grain heads, boosting yield.

Sucking insects do their good work in another way. In some cases they increase the production of useful hormones by plants, Harris says. Two scientists he cites in his article found that mites placed on plum leaves caused those leaves to grow longer and weigh more than uninfested leaves. It's not clear whether the mites produced the hormones and injected them into the plum leaves, or whether the plum tree itself produced substances in response to the mite attack. But the mites did help the plum leaves to grow better.

These findings—and perhaps others yet to come—may force people to take a whole new look at the role insects play in our lives. Up to now, most people have had an almost hysterical reaction to insects, even the good ones. Many gardeners and farmers don't want any insects on their plants and will spray at the first sign of infestation.

We've known for years how unwise a totally insect-free environment is, but now a whole new dimension is added to our comprehension of insect activity. Even the attackers may be doing us a favor! Not always, of course, but at least sometimes.

Unfortunately, it is still too soon to expect everyone to accept the organic gardeners' and farmers' doctrine of peaceful coexistence with insects, but commercial growers are beginning to think that biological control and integrated pest management (combining reduced use of chemicals with biological control) are worth considering. Biological control gets pest interested in knocking out each other instead of the farmers' crops. The technique has been used since 1762, when mynah birds were sent from India to the island of Mauritius to control a plague of red locusts. It has many advantages. Most important, biological control doesn't involve toxic chemicals likely to contaminate food. Furthermore, farmers like its economics. Chemical insecticides are often very expensive, and if the farmer can cut down on the number of sprays needed each year he can pocket a sizable amount of cash. Of great interest, too, is the permanence of biological control. Once you bring together an insect with his natural enemies you have him under control—unless someone moves in with insecticides and kills off the predators.

Many farmers never realized the tremendous benefits of natural biological control until they started spraying and killed off the predator insects, which are usually more sensitive and easily killed than the plant-eating pests. When the pests returned in greater numbers each year, farmers and entomologists discovered what they had done.

The worst insect pests are those which have migrated to new areas, leaving behind their natural enemies. In their homelands such insects may have been only minor pests, but loosed in a new location without predators, they multiply rapidly and greatly damage crop plants. The list of foreign insect visitors to the United States includes the European corn borer, the Japanese beetle, the gypsy moth, and the codling moth. When insects like these break loose in a new country, we must go to their homelands, find their natural enemies, and bring them back to keep the escaped pest in check. That kind of study requires very experienced people, careful research, and plenty of money. We have been moderately successful in introducing enemies of the Japanese beetle here, and we are making progress in taming the European corn borer and the gypsy moth through biological controls.

In some areas, the predators of such insects are being raised and distributed by federal and state action groups. A Maryland research and development project centering on a parasite of the

Mexican bean beetle was so successful it has evolved into an annual program run by the state Department of Agriculture.

The same method can be used against native insects, although the potential is not as great. Biological control specialists of the University of California are convinced insects can be found in other countries which will attack and control some of our native pests. We have only scratched the surface so far. Even though biological control has been practiced for about ninety years in this country, we have tried to import natural enemies for only a fraction of the six hundred pest insects which attack our crops. Money is the primary limiting factor. Because natural methods often don't require the use of commercial products, industry tends to look on biological control as having less business potential than pesticide development.

Yet in the mid-1960s, the President's Science Committee estimated that for every dollar spent on classical biological control in California between 1923 and 1959, thirty dollars was returned in accrued benefits. The comparable return on pesticides was reckoned as five dollars at best. More recently, a five-year program to eradicate screwworm in the southeastern United States saved at least ten dollars for each one spent, while every dollar used for biological control of the Hessian fly has been returning fifteen dollars annually.

Transplanting insect enemies is not the only method of biological control. Much is being done to find diseases that will decimate insect populations. Once found, the disease organisms are cultured and spread over fields in the same manner as chemical insecticides. A few kinds of biological control that could result in a marketable product are attracting some interest. Milky spore disease of the Japanese beetle was one of the first such disease organisms to be commercialized. *Bacillus thuringiensis,* an organism said to be effective against several different pests, is now being sold in many areas. But in their authoritative book, *Biological Control of Insect Pests and Weeds* (1964, Reinhold), Professor Paul DeBach and his colleagues from the University of California at Berkeley and Riverside appear concerned that insect pathogens will attract too much interest, to the detriment of encouragement of natural enemies, a field which they think holds great promise for dramatic, permanent, and inexpensive future benefit.

Yet another kind of biological control involves using the airborne hormones given off by insects. There is definite proof that insect behavior is profoundly influenced, if not completely controlled, by pheremones, the particular chemical substances used by organisms of the same species to communicate with each other. Scientists have successfully used sex attractants of this kind to attract destructive male insects for sterilization or to distract them so they fail to find and mate with females. Gardeners and small-scale orchardists also are using various pheremones to bait traps.

A garden that is too clean can be the enemy of helpful insects. The dust stirred up by cultivation can choke them to death. Whenever possible in orchards and gardens, keep a sod cover where helpful insects can find refuge. Even small weed patches at the garden's edge can prove helpful. In fact, experimental evidence suggests that in addition to harboring beneficial bugs, weeds may actually repel the more destructive ones. Much of the work behind this theory has been done by Dr. Miguel Angel Altieri, a scientist formerly with the prestigious research institution *Centro Internacional de Agricultura Tropical (CIAT)* of Cali, Colombia, and now an assistant professor at the University of California at Berkeley.

Two laboratory tests and nine field experiments at *CIAT* have shown in a preliminary way the surprising insect-controlling power of weeds. In one lab test where bean leaves were offered to leafhoppers both alone and mixed with grassy weed leaves, 80 percent of the insects moved away from the grass and bean leaf mixture. Only 20 percent stayed to munch on the mixture of bean plants and weeds. That's a remarkable demonstration.

When small amounts of weeds were allowed to grown in field, insects were also repelled. In a planting of corn and beans together, leafhoppers were reduced by 40 to 53 percent. Keep in mind that the weeds were controlled carefully. They were not allowed to get big enough to cut into the yields of the corn and beans. Allowing weeds to grow in corn also reduced cutworm damage—by a large 68 percent.

Whatever else we do, it's important that we stop thinking of insects as all bad, as creatures to be completely destroyed so man can live in peace on this earth. We must have plenty of bugs in our fields. The predators need something to feed on, so there must always be a few pest insects around. We must make up our minds to live peaceably with these few pests, and even share our bounty with them. Much of the trouble we have today comes from demanding food that is absolutely untouched by insects. Insect markings often affect only the appearance of fruit, not its basic quality, whereas our phobia of them has resulted in produce laden with insecticide residues.

Biological control offers not a complete victory against the insects, but a cease-fire. To put it into effect will require money, clever scientific planning, time, and willingness to learn to live with insects.

The Chemicals Keep Coming

Pesticide is a dirty word in much of American society. Many millions of people now realize that the synthetic chemicals used to kill insects and to control weeds and plant diseases are often persistent poisons with great potential to do harm.

Most farmers, however, continue to be enmeshed in a production system that makes heavy use of pesticides. The spray rig is still used extensively on all but organic farms. DDT, aldrin, dieldrin, and some other poisons have been barred for certain uses, but other chemicals are being phased in. Indeed, an estimated thirty-five thousand pesticides made of some fifteen hundred chemicals remain on the market. More than a hundred of these weed and insect killers are suspected to be carcinogenic, and the Environmental Protection Agency admits that it will take about twelve to fifteen years to complete the review of all currently registered pesticides.

In the meantime, pesticides are steadily being documented as a major health hazard. Hundreds of pounds of dioxin, one of the most toxic chemicals ever made, together with huge quantities of other pesticides, were among the twenty thousand tons of chemicals buried in the infamous Love Canal in upstate New York. In Memphis, Tennessee, where pesticide and herbicide production is the second most important industry, people living close to the factories and to their waste dumps have a very high incidence of cancers, birth defects, miscarriages, and other health problems similar to those experienced at Love Canal.

In his devastating book, *Laying Waste: The Poisoning of America by Toxic Chemicals*, Michael H. Brown describes numerous other major toxic waste sites. Pesticides are prominent in many of them and make up a goodly part of the sixty million tons of poisons being dumped each year in our country. Inevitably, these deadly wastes and runoffs from massive applications of high-nitrogen chemical fertilizers find their way into our water supplies.

According to a survey published in 1977 by the Food and Drug Administration, pesticide residues are also being discovered in increasing amounts in our food—especially in products coming from animals, which are at the top of the food chain and therefore have concentrated amounts of such pollutants stored in their fat. The most frequently found pesticide in the 117 food items sampled around the country was dieldrin. Levels had increased by 10 percent in one year, while residues of heptachlor epoxide doubled in that time.

Reports of the mounting toll exacted by pesticides on human health and life are becoming commonplace. And to counter our growing uneasiness and defend the multibillion dollar farm market for these products, the chemical industry has used tremendous promotional muscle.

Must we accept poison along with our vegetables, meat, grain, and other foods in order to have enough to eat? Yes, we most certainly must, if we believe an advertisement that has been run in business publications by the Pennwalt Corporation. Pennwalt makes good stuff like methyl parathion, one of the most toxic of all pesticides, and something called Decco, which is put on the fruits and vegetables you see in supermarkets to make them look fresh when actually they are quite old. Pennwalt doesn't let the word spread around that such chemicals may be dangerous, or not necessary, so it's been carrying on an institutional advertising campaign in magazines that are read by influential people.

"Natural farming is perfectly all right, as long as you believe in natural famine," says the ad's headline. I won't comment about that statement just yet. Let's go to the first paragraph of the copy.

"Every year American farmers plant over a billion acres of crops, but each year over 40 percent—almost 500 million acres—is destroyed by pests. Our crop losses in terms of acreage, equal the combined area of Texas, California, Oregon, Washington, and Idaho."

That doesn't strike me as a very good example with which to start off an advertisement plugging pesticides. Most certainly the 40 percent of all cropland Pennwalt speaks of is not being farmed organically. (Only about 1 percent of United States farmland is handled organically today.) No, those 500 million acres, on which we are told all the crops are lost, are being sprayed. And the information I have indicates they are sprayed very heavily. But still the bugs and other pests move right in. In large measure they've gotten used to the poisons, and now have an amazing and frightening amount of resistance.

Let's move on to the next paragraph.

"Even in the face of this tragic waste," says Pennwalt, "it has become fashionable, in some circles, to criticize the use of chemical pesticides and fertilizers."

Well, who wouldn't criticize chemicals that don't work! Forget for a moment their hazardous nature and think of the farmer shelling out ever-increasing amounts of his usually borrowed capital for insecticides that the bugs gobble up and digest as easily as they masticate his lettuce leaves. No wonder the fashionable talk out in farm country gravitates toward gripes about the high cost and low effectiveness of farm chemicals.

The rest of the advertisement goes on to talk about why ag-chemicals are "essential to the survival of the four billion people on this planet," and how the Pennwalt brand of methyl parathion is "less toxic for those who apply it." Still toxic, mind you, but less toxic. It ends with a final blast at the natural-is-better mentality. "We don't think there's anything natural about not having enough food in this world," Pennwalt's copywriter said.

What does all this mean? Why is a large chemical outfit like Pennwalt blasting away with big bucks in *Business Week* at people who spread the fashionable idea that farm chemicals are bad? Could it be that organic growers are getting so numerous that they are beginning to have an impact on the marketing and advertising thinking of the big chemical companies?

That doesn't seem at all likely to me. While the organic movement is growing, my guess is that Pennwalt isn't worried just yet about organic philosophy making inroads on their sales. I believe that their prime concern is that conventional farmers are soon going to get fed up with buying and using chemicals that don't do their job as well as they used to. Those farmers—the ones who grow crops on the five hundred million sprayed acres which still get destroyed each year—are reaching the end of their rope. They are going to cut back on chemicals, and that will hurt sales.

An interesting point is that this institutional advertising campaign was run in *Business Week*, which is probably read by very few farmers. It is my opinion that the ads weren't talking to farmers at all, but to bankers. Most bankers making loans to farmers insist that those farmers use pesticides to protect their crops. If the bankers of America ever learned their ecology and realized that crops could be grown as well or better without chemicals, that would indeed be bad news for Pennwalt. Hence, the importance of making sure the "fashionable" talk about how chemicals don't work so well anymore doesn't spread to bank boardrooms.

Now let's return to the "natural famine" business in the ad's headline. That's total hogwash. Evidence is accumulating rapidly from unbiased sources that unless natural farming catches on pretty darn fast, we're going to see the biggest famine ever in the history of the world. The whole process of producing food on a large scale is out of kilter, and the fact that bugs are learning to shrug off even the most toxic poisons is only part of the picture.

We have to start being concerned about the effects of chemicals on agriculture worldwide, as well as about what happens to the crops in our own garden or in one farmer's fields. The use of chemicals on farms is becoming so widespread around the world that there is a danger that they could combine to form a chemical soup which would have the power to poison the whole productive biosphere in a few decades. That process could be caused not only by the use of pesticides, but by the general intensification of agriculture as more food is grown each year to supply the world's increasing population. Another factor contributing to the threat of global biotic degradation is the massive cutting down of forests. The power of trees to purify the environment is being lost, and the land they occupied is increasingly being given over to chemicalized cropping.

The scenario described above is not a thought hatched in my organic-oriented brain. No, I got it from a technical paper published in 1979 in the journal *Ecotoxicology and Environmental Safety*. The author is F. P. W. Winteringham, and the paper's title is "Agroecosystem—Chemical Interactions and Trends." Winteringham works for the Chemical Residues and Pollution Program of the United Nations in Vienna, Austria. If all the farmers and gardeners now spraying pesticides would read that article, I'm sure they would begin to wonder what kind of world they are creating for their children, their grandchildren, and other generations yet to come.

Also, if farmers had to pay all the costs that are incurred by society as a result of their use of pesticides, you would hear plenty more about how bad the chemicals are. An excellent analysis of those costs was presented recently in the book, *Pest Control: Cultural and Environmental Aspects*, by David Pimentel and John H. Perkins. It was published in 1980 by Westview Press for the American Association for the Advancement of Science. Pimentel and Perkins state that the direct damages that pesticides do to the environment and to society add up to an annual cost of $839 million. If you combine that with the $2.2 billion farmers pay directly for pesticides each year, you can see that a large part of the cost is being borne by innocent bystanders, like yourself.

I am convinced that a transition to chemical-free agriculture can be made within a few years, and with no threat of famine. In the nine years we've had the 305-acre Organic Gardening and Farming Research Center, all the land we didn't need for our test plots has been farmed organically with high yields by Ben Brubaker, our Mennonite neighbor.

Last year, Brubaker's corn yields on some fields were within ten bushels per acre of the highest achieved by any farmer in Pennsylvania. Victor Wegrzyn, a Penn State University student working on a Ph.D. in agronomy, monitored Brubaker's yields and tried to improve them by adding nitrogen fertilizer. In no instance did the nitrogen increase yields, because the organic methods Brubaker was using were allowing that soil to produce every bit of food it possibly could.

No toxic sprays are used, and the farm has remarkably low populations of harmful insects. Some of our field trials aimed at finding the insect-repelling power of certain plants didn't work out so well because not enough harmful insects showed up to be counted with statistical reliability. This year, we're hoping that it's a better year for the bugs so we can get on with our counting.

The users of methyl parathion and similar insecticides should have problems like that!

Gardening for Security

By helping you to avoid toxic pesticides and harmful fertilizers, organic gardening can contribute a lot to your health security. Moreover, as drought and soaring production costs send grocery bills skyward, food put by is beginning to look more and more like a mainstay of financial security.

In fact, a while back the financial section of the *Sunday*

Telegraph, an English newspaper, recommended an investment portfolio consisting entirely of canned and bottled foods. Put your money where your mouth is, the paper suggested. "You can't eat share certificates, and you can't eat fine art," said the editors. "But a portfolio of food will always have an alternate use."

Rising prices for food make such an investment more than a joke and also more than a suggestion that you hoard food. From the potential investor's point of view, it's hard to overlook the profit-making possibilities in owning a commodity that went up in price by 39 percent over the past five years and is conservatively estimated to jump by at least 45 percent over the next five. And, as the newspaper said, if prices do go down, your investment is not really a loss. You can eat your assets.

Investment in food is nothing new, although supermarket psychology has changed things somewhat. In earlier times food was a popular investment commodity, and it is becoming more valuable rapidly. Money, as we are now relearning, has its ups and downs as something to put your confidence in. Even gold is not a sure thing in these days of astoundingly high interest rates. But food—that's something that always has had value and always will.

I still remember clearly the fantastic stocks of food I used to see in Pennsylvania Dutch farm homes. Usually just the kitchen was heated, not only to save money but to provide plenty of cool space in various parts of the house to store smoked meats, fruit, and other food. The cellar was lined with canning jars full of a wide variety of foods, and there were always several crocks of sauerkraut. Every farm had a root cellar, stocked with baskets of potatoes, onions, carrots, apples, pears, and other fruit. Grain for flour and corn for meal were kept in bins in the barn and were taken to nearby water-powered mills to be ground. Many of these farms were dairies, so milk was always available. Needless to say, a kitchen garden got plenty of well-rotted manure, and literally bulged with vegetables in season.

There's been quite a change in the past twenty years. Farmers are now buying most of their food in stores, even here in Pennsylvania. Changing eating habits demand more processed foods, restaurant meals, and convenience items. There's been a

strong trend toward turning over more food processing and preparation to factories and shops, and that's been a big cause of the
steady rise in food prices. Factory handling of food is not cheap,
especially in these days of rising wage rates, shipping costs, and
expenses for raw materials like tin-plated steel cans. The great
majority of America's food is now stored in warehouses and is
in the processing pipeline. Less is tucked away in home storage.

Worldwide uncertainty about our economic future is swing-
ing things around, though, and the old habits are
returning—forced upon people by the inflation crunch. Home
food gardening is now looked on as much more than a hobby,
or as a way to get the kind of good-tasting food you used to get
from local truck gardeners but can't find any more. Gardening
now is basic production of food. People are digging up part of
their lawns to be able to save money on vegetables and fruits.
They are recycling the organic wastes of the household and yard
through a compost heap, to get free fertilizer. Cellars are again
filling with canning jars, and freezers are bulging with home-
produced food. The food-storing habits of the old days are coming
back.

The garden is the center of this new effort to bring the
production of food back into the hands of the family that will eat
it. But a garden is only the beginning. In both a tangible and
symbolic way, a garden points toward a wide variety of activities
that can create remarkable benefits in personal security. That is
especially true when a garden is run on organic principles. Then,
fertilizer is for the most part made from local sources of wastes
by composting and mulching. An organic garden doesn't, like
a golf-course fairway, take food from the world's hungry by drawing on the limited supplies of nitrogen and other fertilizers made
from oil.

Instead, it leads directly to the idea of homesteading, where
improved personal productivity becomes part of a family's whole
lifestyle. In homesteading, the garden remains the center of your
thoughts, but food is produced, processed, and stored in all possible ways.

Most important of all, the ethic of homesteading encourages
people to examine more carefully their lifestyle, and especially

their patterns of consumption. We Americans have allowed ourselves to develop an extremely wasteful way of life. Until recently, energy and food were relatively cheap, creating little incentive for anyone to plan a frugal way of life. As a result, we do too much traveling both for work and amusement. And we use too much horsepower to move ourselves around. We create fantastic amounts of waste, much of which must be carried long distances for disposal. We have constructed a way of life that gives almost no thought at all to the joy that can come from simplicity, smallness, quiet, and meditation. Overconsumption is the major ingredient in our present lack of security.

Things are changing, of course, and in ways that go far beyond the environment of a garden. But I think that the homesteading ethic is the best handle for the average person today to grasp to get both the feeling and reality of security. We need to look anew at the kinds of food people used to store and eat regularly before the days of our energy intoxication. Cornmeal, not gasoline, was the fuel of our forefathers. It was the grist of the past homesteads of America, and can again find an honored place on our table as a basic food, not just as a breading for fried chicken. Why? Because you can still buy a twenty-five-pound bag of fresh, whole, fragrant meal for roughly eight dollars, and can turn it into food that would cost you more than forty dollars if you bought it in cans or boxes sold in small units and printed with fancy labels. What brand should you get? Local mills in many parts of the country are again selling meal made from the kind of corn that is most suited for eating in bulk. You will have to look around and do some experimenting until you find what tastes good to you, but you certainly won't decide on the gritty, degerminated meal that is so commonly seen in supermarkets.

You can get yourself a small hand mill for less than thirty dollars and start grinding some of your own flour and meal. It will be hard work at first, but your muscles will strengthen, inspired to keep working by the taste of food you may remember from your childhood. Seeking greater security, you can begin growing your own corn and grain for milling. More people are doing it every year, creating a demand for small threshing and harvesting machines that I hope will soon be filled. On a minor scale, you can harvest and process these foods for storage by hand, using simple tools like rakes, scythes, and hand shellers.

To some people all this sounds like hard work, but to great numbers it is pure enjoyment. Gardening is more than merely the production of food. It is one of the few tangible ways the average person can witness the thrill of producing something beautiful and useful from basic raw materials like manure, earth, and dead leaves. The gardening-homesteading way of life is fun, not only because of the thrill of production and the solid satisfaction of building your own secure reserves, but because it is tied in with relief from hectic old habits of waste and consumption.

There is nothing that matches a garden as a symbol of frugality and the ending of waste. To help you see that idea more clearly, I've listed six ways that a garden saves. (Maybe you can think of some others.)

First, land is saved by a garden. Almost every home that is not in an inner city (as well as many that are) has land going to waste. Most often the waste takes the form of a too large lawn that takes time and gasoline in the mowing. A garden, producing food, ends that waste. The land becomes productive instead of being just part of the scenery around the house.

Time is saved by a garden. Perhaps it would be more accurate to say that time is salvaged. Hours that otherwise would melt away in some unaccountable fashion are put to constructive use in a garden. Every one of us, no matter how busy we think we are, has niches of time which fit perfectly into garden activity. There, those leisure moments become productive and also restful.

Another garden saving is of energy. True, some garden machines use gasoline or electricity, but think for a moment of the big picture. The food produced in a garden doesn't travel thousands of miles to your table. Neither does it go through energy-expensive processing or packaging. And while you may pour a few quarts of fuel into your tiller from time to time, if you weren't doing that you might be using many gallons pursuing some other leisure-time goal. I would guess that home gardening is one of the most energy-saving forms of outdoor recreation you could find.

The biggest garden saving is of waste itself. Another person's trash is the gardener's gold. Garbage, leaves, grass clippings, manure, rained-on hay, cut weeds, sawdust, even hair trimmings, are all grist for the compost pile. Put these wastes in a corner of your garden or an out-of-the-way place in your backyard. Make it about six inches deep. Then spread on a two-inch covering of manure or other high-nitrogen material. Over that goes a sprinkling of topsoil. Repeat the layering process time and again, each time using six inches of green matter, two inches of manure, garbage, or something rich in nitrogen, and the sprinkling of topsoil.

The dimensions of your heap can vary, depending on the amount of waste you have to build it with. The primary goal is to make the pile wide enough and high enough—and also rich enough—so microorganisms can grow rapidly inside it and cause the pile to heat. If you shred wastes before making the pile and turn it every few days, you can have finished compost in as short a time as two weeks. That's very rapid transformation from bothersome waste to the best kind of fertilizer.

I don't think I'm stretching a point in saying that a garden saves water, rainfall in particular. Without gardens to fall on, that water would miss doing some real good during its oft-repeated cycling from sky to earth and back. Water, more people are saying, is going to prove more valuable than oil one of these days, so we've got to think hard about using it well. If you're in a dry area, drip irrigation, which meters water slowly to each plant, should be part of your saving plan.

And finally, a garden can save money. You can garden frugally, turning wastes into compost and mulch, and concentrating on the simple culture of food plants. Perhaps if you had to pay yourself for your time, the balance would tip the other way, but if you view your involvement as a hobby, then gardens grown from recycled resources can save real money in these days of outrageously priced produce. According to a Gallup survey done by Gardens for All, the total value of food grown in American gardens in 1979 was $13 billion. The average value of the produce grown by a family with a garden was $325, while the median garden size was only 595 square feet. Their gardening expenses? Just $19.

While an organic garden is by definition a focus of conservation, improvements can almost always be made to increase the return on this "investment." I've already mentioned mulching and drip-irrigation as antiwaste techniques. Mulching keeps moisture in the soil and prevents weed growth, while drip-irrigation lets you put water only where it will do the most good. But there are plenty of other techniques that will reduce waste.

Succession planting will let you grow several different plants in the same area . You make better use of available sunlight and nutrients, while often discouraging weeds and insects.

Though such pests cause much garden waste, their damage can be reduced with the help of some careful planning. Rotating your "crops," and even growing grain in part of your garden for one season, can cut back drastically on weed problems. (Weeds are shaded out by a dense planting of grain, so there will be fewer weed seeds to sprout the next year. It's an idea worth trying.) Dozens of natural ways can be used to fight or outfox insects, not the least of which is to select types of plants that are resistant to insect attack in your area.

Harvesting at the proper time is also important. Some garden produce is wasted because it passes the peak of goodness before being picked. The Chinese, whom I consider among the world's best gardeners, seldom make that mistake. Vegetables in their markets seem smaller and more tender than ours. They don't have our passion for giantism, which could be why their food tastes so good.

A report on food waste issued a few years ago by the Comptroller General of the United States showed that more fruits and vegetables were thrown out uneaten in the school lunch program than any other kind of food. Fully 35 percent of fruits and vegetables were avoided, compared to 14 percent for meat, 15 percent for bread and butter, and 13 percent for milk. My guess is that the same pattern applies to food eaten at home and in restaurants. Finding some way to get better flavor and crisp tenderness into vegetables as they reach the table would cut down much of our astounding food waste. All told, we lose over $30 billion worth of food a year—far too much considering how stressed most household budgets are these days.

Getting Value from Our Lawns

American lawns sink their roots into some of the world's best-fed soil. Fertilizers are spread on many lawns at rates that make the typical farmer's soil-feeding efforts look miserly by comparison. Where does all that fertility go? If you don't remove the clippings, it just stays there, making your lawn soil richer with each passing year. If cut grass is raked up, the valuable fertility is carted away to a dump, or piled on some nearby vacant field or hedgerow.

Overfertilizing is not the only problem I see when I look at the average lawn. My mind focuses on the expensive, oil-burning equipment used to keep lawns looking neat and the time spent on lawn maintenance. I'm also concerned about the potent pesticides many people spread on the ground around their homes. What harm do they do to the health of adults and children using that lawn? Wouldn't a few weeds or brown patches in the grass be preferable to a possible health hazard?

Of course, lawns do return something for all the effort and money expended on their care. They look nice. They are pleasant to walk over and to play on. And lawns certainly have a psychological value: all that nice, green space helps relax the mind. It separates us from the frustrations of the outside world, both physically and mentally.

Lawns are here to stay. We need them to set off our homes, and to provide an outdoor carpet for rest and recreation. But we don't need giant lawns. I object to the mindless mowing of areas that could be used far more profitably in other ways. Too often, we mow simply because we haven't been imaginative enough to think of better ways to use that space.

When my wife and I had our house built back in the 1950s nobody thought lawns were a wasteful way to use large areas of suburban land. Energy was cheap, so was fertilizer, and inflation was not seen as a threat to our standard of living. A small voice in the back of my head, though, told me that the two acres of land gifted to us by my father were too valuable to be used merely to grow grass.

My answer to that little voice was to plant trees on about a third of the lot, which was unimproved but fertile farmland. I wanted a small forest next to my house, and I wanted it as quickly as possible. So I planted fast-growing trees—mostly pines, poplars, elms, and a few maples and sycamores.

Today my small wood lot is a reality. The trees are big, and getting bigger. But what has grown more is my knowledge of suburban forestry. I've learned that fast-growing trees can have weaknesses. They often die or split apart after twenty years of growth, which is a short time in the life of a forest. Their wood is less useful for fuel—a fact that's important today. My trees were fun to plant and watch grow, but only the trees truly native to my area—the white pines—are doing spectacularly well.

There is a strong possibility that my best approach (handsight is always clear) would have been simply to walk away from the part of my land I wanted to reforest and let nature take its course. Here in the East, land that is not mown reverts to forest over a period of time. First, the grasses grow tall, and native weeds and wildflowers begin to thrive. Trees pop up after a few winters. The first to grow are the types with wind-borne seeds. Then squirrels plant nut trees, and other animals carry in the seeds of shrubs that cling to their fur. Birds can also carry in tree and shrub seeds. If mature trees are growing near the unmowed land, the process of natural succession from grass and weeds to trees will happen in only a few years.

Today, with the energy problem so heavily upon us, that natural approach to landscaping is becoming an attractive alternative to the standard lawn. In fact, it's an important alternative energy strategy. I know of dozens of places in many states where landowners now consciously stop mowing a part of their land, encouraging native trees to become established. Landscape architects are even perfecting systematic ways to use this ad hoc approach.

Richard Harwood, Ph.D, director of the Organic Gardening and Farming Research Center, has been working on several concepts that open the way to very practical uses for lawn space. One that Dick has tested for over two years is the "meadow lawn." An established lawn area is tilled and replanted with plants that grow to limited height, look nice, and pump nitrogen from the air into the soil to maintain or build fertility. The big advantage of the meadow lawn is that it cuts maintenance. You need to mow it only once or twice a year. It may look shaggy at first because we're so used to the "crew cut" lawn, but the wildflowers and wildlife that enliven a meadow lawn create a totally different kind of visual interest.

The Research Center people have also developed and tested a much quicker way to put a lawn to work. They have found that almost any lawn area can be made into a vegetable garden without digging up the turf. The method is so new that it doesn't yet have a name, although it might be called a lawn garden or a pointed stick garden. All you do is make holes in the sod wherever you want to plant corn, tomatoes, squash, or similar large-growing vegetables. The seeds sprout and the plants thrive, provided you mow the grass between the rows and mulch with lawn clippings, leaves, hay, or even sawdust.

Sounds crazy, doesn't it? But the lawn garden is not a screwball idea. It was suggested to us by horticultural scientists at Cornell University who tried the method in their own backyards and found it worked well. At our Research Center, we've run lawn garden tests for three complete seasons and found that turf, if kept under control, is not an obstacle to production. Our gardens-in-the-grass produced just as much food per unit of land area as did comparable regular gardens planted in tilled land. Of course, if you want to use this method and enjoy digging, you can till several narrow strips across your lawn and plant your garden in them. But leave grass growing between the rows. The sod stops erosion, keeps mud off your feet in wet weather, and helps improve soil fertility, especially if there is some clover in your lawn. Why? Grass clippings from the mowed spaces between rows can be raked around your vegetable plants, forming a nitrogen-rich mulch.

I realize that allowing part of your lawn to revert to meadow or forest, or planting tomatoes in your turf, may sound like strange ideas at first. But maybe they won't seem so strange if you try to visualize these ideas as partners of the same kinds of changes now affecting home design itself. A new earth-sheltered home makes more productive use of the land than does a 1950 split-level. So the space around these new energy-efficient homes should be used in a similarly modern manner. And there's no reason at all why the yard around an older home can't be retrofitted with energy-efficient landscaping.

We're now in the process of doing that kind of retrofitting to over two acres of land just outside my office window. The front yard of our building has been converted to meadow lawn and a natural forest area. (At this point the forest is less than two years old, and without trees.) Our plan is to mow the meadow lawn only once a year. The forest portion will never be mowed again.

Shortly after we stopped mowing the land, town officials cited us for violating the local weed ordinance. That law gave the town authority to mow our lawn if any growth not planted for some "useful purpose" achieved a height of fifteen inches or more. Here we were, trying to save energy, catch more rainwater, increase soil fertility, and produce some useful wood, and we run afoul of a law that is about as modern as another local ordinance requiring horses to walk through covered bridges.

Of course we didn't just roll over and give in to the heavy hand of local grass regulation. We went to court seeking a permanent injunction to keep Emmaus municipal mowers off our land, and I'm glad we did. The trial motivated us to accumulate a bigger case against the mowed lawn than I ever suspected existed. And we got plenty of good publicity, including a funny story by Calvin Trillin in *The New Yorker*. Happily, we won our case, with the judge ruling that because of its experimental nature and its educational value for local school children our meadow lawn was indeed useful.

There probably is a weed ordinance in your town, too. You can visit your town hall to read all its obnoxious details. Maybe your ordinance is a liberal one, and your project won't be barred by its strictures. If necessary, though, I hope you'll work against such regulation. Don't let a small, ill-conceived law get in the way of advanced biomass technology, which is what lawn gardening really is.

Be careful, though, not to ignore your neighbors. "Let them know what you're doing and why you're doing it," advises Carol Smyser McHarg, the author of a book soon to be published by Rodale Press called *Nature's Design*. If you cheerfully explain yourself at the outset, nobody will think you're trying to ruin the neighborhood. If you are seen outside mulching your lawn garden or planting the seeds of native wildflowers, your changes stand a better chance of acceptance. Be especially attentive to your borders. Rather than run your new lawn right up to your neighbor's carefully clipped turf, maintain a perimeter of traditional green or plant a hedgerow.

Neighborliness on your part serves two purposes. It reduces the risk of an anonymous complaint to local officials, and it guards your project against a sour note. Making a new lawn would be much less fun if it meant losing an old friend in the process.

Coping with the Weather Changes Ahead

rganic gardening practices may make even more sense in the future than they do now if certain long-range weather predictions turn out to be accurate. Careful studies of weather records going back far into the past reveal a rather startling picture of the stability and favorable nature of the weather we've enjoyed for the past forty to fifty years. True, there have been droughts, floods, cold spells, and heat waves all over the place during the past four or five decades. There always have been those weather extremes and there always will be. But on the average, during our lifetimes we have enjoyed some of the best weather for farming, gardening, and all kinds of food production that is likely to occur in any but a totally utopian world.

Take a look at historical weather records that go back more than fifty years, and you begin to see what real climate variations can be like. In some of the major crop areas, there were such frightening things as midsummer frost and droughts that dried up all the wells for miles around. Many people died, not necessarily from starvation but from infectious diseases that preyed on malnourished, unhealthy bodies. Weather experts agree that this picture of past climate is real, and not based on people's hazy memories of hardship experienced during their youth. "Weather in the major crop-growing areas of the United States has been uniformly good for many years," U.S. Weather Service climatologist J. Murray Mitchell, Jr. said a few years ago. "It's almost a fluke, in a climate that over the longer run has varied much more than that."

A similar view comes from Louis M. Thompson of Iowa State University, who published an article on climate change in *Science*. He says that there has been a cooling trend recently, but that it doesn't threaten grain yields or other food production nearly as much as the variable weather we are likely to start experiencing soon. Dr. Thompson says that there have been two fine-weather decades leading up to current times, and they have bred "dangerous complacency with new agricultural technology that is ill-equipped to cope with weather that won't conform to the expected 'norm'."

Note the quotation marks around that word norm. They're important, because probably the biggest part of our problem about weather is the general view that "normal" weather is logical to expect and really does occur. That in itself is the basic false assumption about climate that people make, some experts feel.

"It is rather rare to find a year that meets the definition of normal," Dr. James D. McQuigg said at a world food conference at Iowa State. Dr. McQuigg was formerly the director of the Center for Climatic and Environmental Assessment in Columbia, Missouri—a federally connected weather agency that specializes in looking at weather records and trying to decide what they mean. He told food conferees that he had examined forty-four different years' worth of temperature and rainfall data for Iowa and failed to find even one year that could reasonable be called normal. And that's during this recent period that has been so favorable and moderate.

He did say, as you might expect, that a lot of those years were close to "some reasonable range of normal," and when that happened farmers got optimum yields. But he cautioned agricultural leaders not to design farm management systems based on the assumption that the climate will remain near normal. That can "lead to some very great difficulties," he pointed out. In other words, there is the distinct likelihood that some people are going to go hungry if we expect "normal" weather to continue, but fail to experience it.

Understanding the bad effects that more climate variation can have on food production is difficult for many farmers and gardeners because we already expect seasonal and other changes. Even if there were such a thing as a normal year, we would still shiver at times in the winter and swelter in the summer. So what's so different about a little more variation?

The difference would be that some of our crops would never reach maturity, and perhaps not even get a decent start in the spring. Farm crops tend to hug the edges of the seasons in their climatic requirements. Plants are the most efficient of all collectors of solar energy, and big yields depend on having them collect as much of that energy as possible. So most of the grains, beans, and other crops are bred to stay out there in the field for longer periods than garden crops. The newer types of corn, which farmers have grown in recent years, are still moist when harvested and have to be dried artificially for best storage. That long-season characteristic is bred into corn varieties to maximize production.

Some clear examples of what can happen are given in a Central Intelligence Agency study of climatological research, which was pried loose from that body by New York Congressman Fred Richmond, a member of the House Agriculture Committee and sponsor of the National Soil Fertility Program in 1975. The CIA points out that European farms now support an average of three people per arable hectare (about 2.5 acres). If the temperature declined only 1° Celsius, that figure would be cut to two people per hectare.

China would suffer even more from climate variation, according to the CIA. In that country, seven people are now living off the food produced on each hectare. A shift of 1° Celsius would mean only four could be supported—a drop of 43 percent.

How about the effect of climate variation on United States food production? It is a measure of our cocksure confidence in the never-failing bounty of the American breadbasket that such questions didn't get much consideration in the CIA report. There is a general feeling that climate here is so favorable that such "slight" changes won't cause any big problems. But nature is sometimes strange and extreme in its ways. The rains can fail here as well as in India—as many of our farmers learned through huge crop losses in 1980.

What should be done to prepare for the future weather problems that are widely expected to occur? A suggestion heard often is the creation of food reserves. Because of the pressure of population expansion, worldwide food stocks are at a very low point. During the era of abundance of the 1950s and 1960s, the world had a 105-day supply of grain and other food on hand. But now our reserves of food are much lower. Crop failures could therefore have more devastating effects than they did in the past.

I am in favor of improving national food reserves, but we shouldn't look on that approach as a real solution to the problem. There are so many billions of people on the earth today that accumulating even a one-year supply of food would call for an enormous extra effort of both production and storage. Centralized food reserves can also become political footballs, kicked around for personal gain by national leaders and speculators while poor people go hungry.

A far better approach is to multiply the number of people who are able to produce at least some of their own food in gardens. For literally dozens of reasons, gardens are much more secure and reliable sources of food in times of climatic extremes than are farms.

Gardens get close, personal management, which means that a variety of measures can be taken to cope with bad weather. In times of drought, more garden plants can be mulched to conserve moisture, and irrigation water can be applied exactly where and when needed. When winter threatens to come early, plants can be harvested and stored, or protected in a variety of ways. More gardeners are getting into greenhouse food production, with an emphasis on well-insulated or solar-heated greenhouses. That kind of gardening will become more important as we experience a wider range of "normal" weather extremes.

There are other important weather facts about gardens. Soil in gardens is usually more fertile than on farms, which helps crop management enormously. Plants in gardens grow faster and yield much more per unit of space used. Even in a season of the worst possible weather, a garden is not likely to be a total failure. The variety of plants grown in gardens is so large, and the options to substitute and vary strategies are so many, that gardening is likely to be productive in seasons when farmers are experiencing severe failures.

New systems of fertilizing and cropping are making gardening even more weather-resistant and efficient than it has been and could boost the significance of gardening as at least a partial solution to world food problems. Fertilizer placement is now known to be extremely important to crop growth. Whether you use natural or artificial fertilizers, they will do more good if placed close to the root zone, protected from the elements and conveniently central to the plant's feeding area. Forming fertilizers into balls of mud or compost and then placing them in the root zone is a method now widely used in underdeveloped countries and destined to spread here soon. Even extreme floods aren't likely to wash away fertilizer applied in that way.

Humus is almost a miracle substance when it comes to building resistance to weather problems into a food-producing system. It is one of nature's great forces for moderation of environmental extremes that affect the land and plants.

A garden or farm soil packed with ample organic matter will

both absorb excess moisture in times of too much rain and preserve what moisture is available during times of drought. That
effect is easy to understand in theory, because humus is spongelike
in its nature. But I've seen it demonstrated so clearly in practice
that the efficiency of humus in controlling water problems is
engraved on my mind.

When my father bought the Organic Gardening Farm back
in 1942, the soil was depleted of humus because of decades of
exploitative farming practices. Even a mild rain would start strong
streams of water flowing off the fields, through the barnyard, and
even into our basement. When I would try to walk through a
cultivated field after a rain, the mud would stick to my shoes like
orange glue.

Now, after years of building up the humus in our soil, even
heavy rains present little problem. Water soaks in quickly, and
only during a cloudburst will much water flow off the soil surface.
Nowadays, even during a rain you can walk through a plowed
field in comfort, with clean boots.

Humus also has important temperature-moderating effects
that help improve the yield of both gardens and farms. To understand how that can be possible, you have to think about the
importance of microclimate variations, as well as the big (macro)
changes that pop into most people's minds when they think about
climate.

In any given plant community, there is actually a variety
of tiny climates. A foot or so off the ground there can be a mix
of temperature, humidity, and wind effects which is quite different from the microclimate at the surface of the soil. That kind
of variation is enormously important to the ecology of a garden
or farm field. Less widely known or understood, though, is the
fact that microclimates can be influenced for the better by such
practices as mulching, weed control, and improvement of the
soil's organic content. A richly organic soil, such as is practical
to maintain in almost any garden, will enjoy a favorable microclimate. Even the climate within the upper few inches of the
soil—the all-important microbial life zone—will improve when
organic matter is added. Achieving those effects in gardens is
much easier than on farms, where vast quantities of organic

materials would have to be introduced to have similar climate-improving effects.

One other type of food production is likely to grow in importance as we search for methods that will operate under climatic extremes. That's fish farming, expecially in small ponds. Cattle and other warm-blooded animals are sometimes vulnerable to climatic extremes and variations. They need shelter from rain, wind, sun, and cold; and the more extremes of weather that are experienced, the more elaborate, efficient, and expensive the shelter must be. Much of the food that such animals eat goes to support their body temperature, a side-point also worth considering.

Fish are cold-blooded. They convert food to protein more efficiently than do warm-blooded animals. But—more important—a fish pond can be designed to operate economically under weather extremes. Some fish prefer very cold weather, and others thrive in warmer water. If you choose your stock intelligently, a protein-producing system can be designed that will operate well under climate variations of almost any type.

Combining fish ponds with gardens is going to be an important trend of the future, I'm convinced. The pond itself becomes a temperature-moderating force, expecially when incorporated into a solar greenhouse. Even outdoor ponds can have important positive effects on the microclimates of gardens, keeping the environment cooler during heat waves and slightly warmer during cold spells. An important additional benefit is the fertility that fish excretions add to water. At the Organic Gardening and Farming Research Center, we have found that using pond water for irrigation boosts garden production significantly.

To sum up—we should not expect that the favorable climate we have experienced in the recent past will continue, but there is no need to be fearful of the future as long as we act intelligently. That means designing and using food-production systems which will work well even if Mother Nature doesn't seem inclined to cooperate as well as she has recently.

Stocking Up on Future Food

Important though they are, the probable weather changes ahead are just part of a much larger scenario threatening the future of our food supply. The question is no longer *whether* a food crunch is going to follow on the heels of the energy crisis, but *when*. Optimists say we've got until the year 2000 or even 2010 until our land base declines to the point where even intensive farming methods can no longer produce enough food for the world's expanded population. I'm an optimist, but I can also read statistics. Furthermore, I've learned a lot lately about how a problem like an energy shortage can mix in with another problem, like growing enough food, to make bad news arrive much earlier than expected. The bottom line, according to my reckoning, is that the real crunch is only a few years ahead and spot outbreaks of the problem are here now. It's also clear that getting enough food at reasonable prices has, for some people, been a difficulty for years.

We have trouble seeing the big picture, though. American farmers have produced surpluses of food for a hundred years or more, and are still doing it now. How could it be that surpluses will turn suddenly into shortages? Well, just think back a few years when there was a global glut of oil, and the price for crude at the well was five dollars a barrel. Things can change quickly, and there doesn't have to be an absolute shortage of something people want badly to cause prices to go through the ceiling. Just a hint that there are limits to the supply, and that total needs are beginning to bump against these limits, is enough to change the picture rapidly.

The food problem may even be tougher to cope with than the oil and energy squeeze. Not everyone has to drive a car, and many jobs can be accomplished with little energy use. But every-

one has to eat every day. The number of eaters is increasing at
the rate of 6.2 million a month globally, and 159,000 a month
here in the United States. And our land base is declining. Every
year the United States loses over 3 million acres of agricultural
land to the building of highways, factories, stores, homes, and
other structures. We lose 4.8 billion tons of soil from our agricultural base each year due to erosion, with as many as twenty
bushels of topsoil disappearing for every bushel of wheat harvested
in the state of Washington. Across the length and breadth of our
country we are eating up more land than food, consuming twenty-
five square miles of our agricultural base *every* day.

There are other problems. In some areas water from irrigation is being pumped up from sub-surface storage areas faster
than it's being replaced by rainfall, and the end of that water
supply is in sight. Pollution caused by overuse of chemicals and
such environmental factors as acid rain are raising doubt about
long-term productivity of many farming areas.

One of the worst aspects of the problem, in my opinion, is
that the whole structure of our agriculture and our food processing
and distribution system has evolved the wrong way. Instead of
producing as much food as possible close to where people are,
and recycling mineral-rich and nitrogen-rich wastes back to the
land, everything is spread out over vast distances. Nitrogen is
shipped thousands of miles, while the same nutrient could be
captured from the air right on the farm if leguminous crops were
used in rotation. And we should not forget that phosphate supplies
in the United States are limited. The price for this fertilizer
component has already shot up, and may soon go still higher.
The same holds true for sulphur, also widely used in the manufacture of fertilizer.

Long-distance food shipping is another part of the problem.
Beef producers in the Midwest reportedly can't make money
because the cost of moving meat to the big markets in the East
is so high. Vegetables and fruits are also moved thousands of
miles. That used to make economic sense when gas prices were
low, but now it's just not right. And it will become even more
wrongheaded in the future as transportation costs go still higher.

A final aspect of the problem is that the processing and distribution of food is becoming concentrated in the hands of a few large companies. Back in the 1930s, 40 percent of all Americans lived and worked on farms. In 1979, only 2.8 percent of the entire United States population were living on farms. There are thirty-two thousand food-manufacturing firms in this country, but 75 percent of the food processing profits go to just fifty of them. With each passing year, power over our food system passes into fewer and fewer hands. According to a recent two-year study by the U.S. Department of Agriculture, if present trends continue, fifty companies could own all food manufacturing assets in our country by the year 2000.

Now, I do not believe that there is a conspiracy to cause the destruction of our farmland, or to give control of the food system to a few businessmen, or to contrive energy shortages to increase food prices. But I do believe that many important people are sitting on their hands and not doing much to prevent such happenings, figuring that their organizations will profit mightily when these factors cause a sellers' market in food to occur. That conspiracy could be somewhat passive, in the sense that the participants don't have a clear plan to make it occur. The fact that saving our land for the production of food or decentralizing the control of our food system is not a high priority is clear evidence that there is at least a conspiracy of silence and inaction.

Dan Morgan, writing in the July 1980 issue of *Atlantic*, tends to confirm these suspicions of mine. In his article, "The Politics of Grain," he advocates that the government and the food trade fix prices for United States grain sold in foreign markets to increase our power to use food as a weapon in world trade. He says that our food structure is well along the way toward being ready for that kind of action and claims:

> There are, in fact, striking parallels between the present grain market and the world oil market of the late 1960's, before the OPEC cartel reached maturity. . . . Now, a decade later, in the world grain economy, a handful of companies that resemble the oil giants in their control of communica-

tion, processing plants, depots, transportation, and financial facilities dominate the system that markets the American surplus.

Here at home the possibility of a potential food shortage is more immediate in some states than others, but scarcity could eventually affect our whole country. Massachusetts is particularly vulnerable. It now imports 40 to 50 percent of its food from California. But in twenty years California will have no food available to send to other states because its own population is growing and by then will need all that can be grown there. Massachusetts is also concerned about a rail or truck strike because only a fourteen-day supply of food can be stored within the state. So much for stating the present and potential problems linked to our food system. Let's begin to focus on the solution.

Curbing population growth is important. Fortunately, people seem to be getting that message and some progress is being made. But growth trends are not easily reversed, and it appears certain that both world population and United States population will increase substantially before leveling off.

Therefore it's critical that we change the structure of our food system. So far it has been a mining operation. We are mining the soil of its fertility and draining oil and gas fields of their wealth to get the energy to do that. Mines always become depleted. We can't afford to let our food system just "run out" someday.

Widespread application of organic farming techniques is the way to build permanence into our farms. Organic farming feeds the soil instead of mining it. Humus is built up, creating an intensely alive soil environment that liberates minerals and other nutrients gradually, in ways that allow a soil to remain fertile for many thousands of years. There is also recycling of nutrients. Rotations which include legumes both capture nitrogen from the air and help to prevent erosion. And interplanting wheat or other cereals with legumes means that the nitrogen fixed by the legumes is used immediately by the other crop before it has a chance to wash out of the soil. Using this method organic researchers have been able to produce normal yields with only one-fourth of the normal amount of fertilizer.

What's more, this kind of interplanting produces a legume-grain harvest that is an ideal mixture nutritionally, providing top-quality protein that can take the place of expensive meat. Organic farming also prevents the costly pollution of our soil, water, air, and food because toxic chemicals are not used.

To suggest organic farming as a way to keep food prices down might strike some people as strange, since in today's market organically grown food usually costs more. That is a strictly temporary situation. Conventional farmers are actually burning up their farms to produce today's commodities. They are consuming their capital—the fertility of their land—in order to try to stay solvent financially. That is a giant hidden cost which doesn't show up in your food bills today, but which will have to be paid soon. We are getting close to the danger point now. Organic farmers refuse to sell their soil along with the food they move to market. So their current prices are somewhat higher.

Just how important organic methods can be to our food future is brought out forcefully in the report and recommendations on organic farming issued in late 1980 by the special organic farming study team of the U.S. Department of Agriculture. This study group was appointed in the spring of 1979 by Anson Bertrand, Ph.D., director of the recently created Science and Education Administration of the USDA. The project marked the first time a group of American scientists, economists, and statisticians attempted to take an objective look at organic methods.

Generally speaking, their preliminary conclusions are very favorable. The study team's report dispels the notion that a switch to organic methods would contract the food supply drastically. A total conversion now would reduce production, true, but there would still be enough food for America's needs and some for export. The most constructive parts of the report suggest excellent directions for research and education projects that could make organic farming much more efficient than it is now, without sacrificing the respect for preservation of resources that is so characteristic of organic farmers. Much remains to be done, for all the achievements of organic farming to date have been accomplished largely outside the farm research and education establishment.

One conclusion of the report is that "a total or even a significant shift to organic farming would require overall major changes in the overall structure of agriculture." I agree, and clearly such changes are needed badly to avoid a food crisis that could be much more difficult for us to cope with than the current energy crunch.

Rodale Press has long recognized the need for change in agricultural structure. In fact, we think the whole food system should be changed in ways that will reduce the distance food and food resources are shipped, encourage the eating of more fresh food (which cuts energy needs), and generally convert our food system from a "gas-guzzler" to a leaner, more efficient model that can keep running far into the future. Those changes are also needed, as the USDA team points out, to make organic farming practical for a larger number of farmers.

The question really is not if structural changes of that type can be made. The only doubt is when they will be imposed on us and on our food system by such pressures as rising energy costs, growing population, declining soil fertility, the need for a secure store of food close to where people live, and high prices for fertilizer ingredients, such as phosphorus. If we keep going blindly on our present course—the way we did with automobile design and use in the early 1970s—the switch to a regional and more natural food production system will hit us with overwhelming suddenness, probably having the same kind of impact on our economy and our lives as the stock market crash of 1929. Nobody wants that.

I feel that if we are going to head off that kind of collapse we need to use entirely new methods to guide ourselves toward change. The challenge is great, for we need the courage to look at what, up to now, has been seen as the strongest part of the American resource system—our food production apparatus—and the boldness to decide that it needs a drastic overhauling to be able to serve us well in the future. That is not an easy task. Certainly it is too massive and important a job to be left just to our elected officials, or to farm scientists, farmers, or food companies.

To encourage thinking and action now, while there is still time, a group of Rodale Press researchers has been defining the major problems of our food system, outlining methods for dealing with these problems, and developing techniques that each American family can use to analyze its own food situation. The primary goal of the project is to supply people with facts about the strengths and weaknesses of the American food system—facts which are crucial to the improvement of that system but which have never been gathered in one place for easy use. Researchers and planners also stand ready to serve organizations that are in need of specialized information or want to become active in developing and implementing the project's goals.

This task force on future food is called the Cornucopia Project, after the traditional horn of plenty, which symbolizes abundance. We gave the project that name because we are optimistic that the current trends pointing toward shortage and inflation can be reversed. There remains an enormous potential in this country for the production of food. Although we have lost half of our land, we still have half left, and we also have the people, the climate, and much of the knowledge to create an agriculture and an entire food system that will bring fresh, wholesome food to everyone at reasonable cost.

Plan Your Food Future Now

To give you a better idea of how we can use the information the Cornucopia Project is collecting to improve our food system, take a good look at your fork next time you sit down to eat. Think how useful it is and also how symbolic. A fork is the main tool you use to get food into your mouth. The idea of a fork also symbolizes choice. A road forks in front of you. Choose one of the forking roads, and you get to an entirely different destination than if you had taken the other.

Eating is often a forking experience, in more ways than one. There are choices to be made. Usually the choices are simple and have no permanent impact on us. "Tonight I'll eat fish, and tomorrow chicken." Eventually, all those menu choices even out and add up to nothing significant.

I'm convinced, though, that right now all of us face another kind of food choice—a forking in our food road—that is entirely different. It's a choice that we've not had to make before. Also, we don't have much time to make up our minds. We are moving quickly and the road is dividing before us. We must go one way or another, and this is not one of those "fish today and chicken tomorrow" choices. It is a choice that will determine where our food comes from, how good it is, and especially how much we must pay for it as long as we live. If we don't make up our minds quickly and take the right road, we are likely to spend the rest of our lives being mere passengers instead of navigators. And the journey could be hazardous indeed.

There are hills and valleys in the road ahead of us, and we can't see over all the obstacles. The road maps we have are only of partial usefulness because our journey for food is into the future. We can only guess what detours and washouts may crop up in the roads ahead.

But there is a useful tool of the futurist that we can work with. It is the scenario—a description of a probable future based on attempts to understand how decisions made today change the nature of the "place" we are going to reach at some point in time ahead. The writer of scenarios knows where we have been and tries to show how course corrections now and in the future change the nature of the destination we will arrive at some day. The scenarios are not the same because the decisions that are made along the way to each destination are different. There is no guarantee of total accuracy, of course, because no one can be sure what course-correcting decisions society will make in the future. Nor can we predict acts of God or other unforeseen events.

But I believe scenarios are extremely useful "seat-of-the-pants" tools for navigation into our future.

For simplicity, let's decide that our future food fork has only two prongs, and write simple scenarios for each one. One prong will be the conventional food scenario, which assumes that the food system will move ahead as it has in the past. Farming will be based on widespread and growing use of chemical fertilizers, synthetic pesticides, and other inputs depending heavily on fossil fuel. Soil erosion will persist at its current rapid rate. The number of farms will continue to decline as remaining farms become larger. Food produced on farms will be shipped long distances to processing plants and markets. Fewer people will work on farms and in the food system as a whole. Consumers will go to fewer and fewer stores for their food purchases and will be encouraged to buy types of food that are highly processed for quick use. In other words, the industrialized and high-tech trends of our food past are projected into the future.

My perception of what will happen if this scenario is followed is based on the thinking and planning that have gone into The Cornucopia Project I mentioned in the previous chapter. A very similar projection of our food future is also made in the *Global 2000 Report to the President*, released in late 1980 by the Council on Environmental Quality and the U.S. Department of State. I am also drawing to some extent on the information in a study of the future of United States agriculture completed recently by The Conservation Foundation.

For simplicity's sake, let's just focus on one issue— the cost of food.

Our Cornucopia Project studies suggest that food will become terribly expensive in the future as the amount of good land available for production declines and the number of mouths to feed increases. The Conservation Foundation experts were "guardedly optimistic" that the amount of food available a couple of decades ahead would be adequate. But at a press conference they concluded that "people would have to spend a larger portion of their income for food in the future." *The Global 2000 Report* puts a number on that cost increase for the period just past the year 2000—the beginning of the twenty-first century. "In order to meet projected demand, a 100 percent increase in the real price of food will be required," the report concludes.

Even without the extra impact of inflation, that kind of food-cost increase would be devastating. Imagine a quick shopping trip in 2001! Some friends drop in for the weekend and you need some extra salad ingredients, fruit, and bread. You cash your paycheck at the store and have to pay exactly double in proportion to today's rates for whatever food you need. That scenario doesn't even consider the impact of inflation—just the rise in price caused by the fact that food is in short supply and more people want to buy it.

Let's factor in inflation as well. I heard a government spokesman say recently that we'll be lucky to have 10 percent inflation for quite a while, and I agree. So we'll use 10 percent as our inflation rate out to the year 2000, and base it on the average retail food costs during 1980.

You pick up a couple of heads of California iceberg lettuce. Two for $9.20. Tomatoes are next. Three large ones cost $5.24. Then green onions—$3.78 a bunch. A loaf of bread costs $7.66. A two-pound bunch of bananas sells for $6.56. Finally, a ten-ounce jar of instant coffee comes to $45.06.

Of course, I realize that your wages have gone up some too in those twenty years, but by now we should have learned that prices go up faster than wages in almost all instances. You also need to keep in mind that food is not going to be the only necessity of life that will rise in price. Forecasts of energy, transportation, and housing costs also indicate that people are going to have to "pay a larger percentage of their income" for them. Where all these "larger percentages" are going to come from, I surely don't know.

The major reason the conventional food system scenario is going to lead to such fantastically high food prices is that the base of production—both in land and energy sources—is being consumed as food is produced. We are eating up now the heritage of productive capacity that will be needed even more in a few short years. No wonder prices are going to go up so much.

Fossil fuels are expensive now, and they're going to cost plenty more in future years. The conventional food system relies heavily on fossil fuels for producing fertilizers and pesticides, for powering all the equipment used, and for shipping food long distances to processing plants and markets. Any scenario that is going to lead us toward reasonable food prices in the future will have to cut fuel use in the agriculture system.

What I call the Cornucopian approach to food production does that. Attention to our soil is a vital first step. Soil is now eroding at a terrible rate, and only the large-scale use of synthetic fertilizers is propping up production. Such practices as proper plowing, crop rotation, and the building up of organic matter and nutrients in the soil will permit intensive use of our land for food production, while at the same time preventing erosion and eliminating the need for chemical fertilizers and pesticides. But planning for these changes will take imagination and effort—starting right now. Good land is the only foundation for low-cost food production. If our land continues to disappear, any hope we have of avoiding super-luxury prices for food will disappear with it.

Other elements of a Cornucopian scenario will focus on how that land is used. To head off disastrous price increases, people will have to figure out ways to produce more food close to home. Transporting food long distances is an idea whose time has passed. Soon we simply will not be able to afford the fuel needed to move meat, vegetables, fruit, and other foods thousands of miles.

I hope people see the need quickly for a return to regionalized food production. Right now, we need clear thinking about the Cornucopian scenario, so future towns can be built in ways that will allow them to be food self-reliant. More space for gardening must be planned into housing developments. Space for small, high-intensity farms should be allowed near towns. Ways to recycle garbage and other organic wastes back to the land—to preserve vital fertilizer nutrients—must also be provided for in future building plans.

Food that is eaten fresh, close to where it is grown, can be provided to consumers with much less capital investment than highly processed food. Our nation is going to need all the capital it can muster for energy and for reconstruction of our industrial plants to make them energy-efficient. The food system can be transformed in Cornucopian ways with very little capital— provided people return to the diet of largely fresh foods, eaten in season. We need dozens of scenarios that will create plans for that kind of diet reeducation for different regions of this country.

Processing and storage of food will have to be done at home or in the local community, at least to a large extent. The financial advantages of home food processing and storage systems are great now, but they'll become overwhelming soon. As food prices continue their upward march, only those people who can put their homes or neighborhoods to full use as food system centers will be able to eat well. Education is needed now to teach everyone how to use home and neighborhood resources to provide food security. Along with a revival of what I call home food systems will come a flowering of small-scale shops and processing plants that will prepare the foods produced in each region.

That is just a brief outline of some of the options for change that could be put into a Cornucopian scenario. You probably have other ideas—particularly steps that could make a low-cost and sustainable food system work well in your area.

In the Cornucopian food system, the opportunity to participate is wide open to everyone. There are many exciting new opportunities for commercial food production. While we can't each have our own food business, every one of us can either grow a garden, sprout seeds, bake bread, or do any one of hundreds of other home food production projects.

2 YOU ARE WHAT YOU EAT

You Are
What You Eat

The technological force which is changing our outside environment is also altering and reducing the value of our food. Speaking plainly, we are falling victim to a form of internal pollution, just as we have to external pollution. The production of food itself has been changed through mechanization and chemical manipulation. And we have become separated from the crop in the field by a massive complex of food processing involving not only machines and chemicals but packaging, storage, and selection procedures that often work to lower the nutritional value of food.

Organic gardeners and health-oriented people have long objected to machine-handled food. But our arguments have been countered by industry claims that Americans are the best-fed people on earth. Now we have solid scientific evidence of internal pollution which cannot be refuted by broad claims that supermarket food is the best available.

Three consumer surveys done by the U.S. Department of Agriculture document sad changes in our nutritional status as engineered foods have come to dominate supermarket shelves and dinner tables.

In the first extensive study, done in 1955, 60 percent of Americans were judged to have diets rated "good" in vitamin and mineral content. Only 15 percent had "poor" diets. But when the study was done again in 1965, the results showed that only 50 percent had good diets, and a growing number—20 percent—were in the poor category. That was a very significant decline, indicating that roughly 25 million people suffered a drop in the nutritional value of their diets. The three food substances particularly deficient, the USDA said, were calcium, vitamin C, and vitamin A.

The latest USDA effort was a fifteen-thousand-household survey completed in 1978. Although all the data will not be available until 1982 or later, the preliminary results are mixed. Americans seem to be taking in more of vitamins A, B, and C and more iron than in 1965. But we are getting even less calcium and too much fat, sugar, and salt—ingredients heavily used in processed foods to make them more appealing.

In addition, some nutritionists have expressed the fear that our increased vitamin intake may be coming from enriched rather than natural foods. For instance, nowadays vitamin C appears to be derived not primarily from citrus fruits but from vitamin-C-enriched sodas, punches, and preprepared desserts. The average amount of these foods consumed per person per week in the United States has jumped 144 percent since the 1965 survey. These synthetic foods lack vital trace minerals such as zinc, potassium, manganese, as well as folic acid—nutrients that are vital to well-being but not even monitored in the government studies.

Another, and in some ways more comprehensive, evaluation of our diet was done by Nobel laureate Dr. Roger J. Williams and his colleague Dr. Don R. Davis. The two biochemists used the per capita consumption figures for food in the United States to construct the "average" American diet. They then did a computer analysis comparing this diet profile with that of a high-quality commercial dog food. The two "menus" were compared for their content of thirty-nine growth and maintenance chemicals needed by the human body. The results were shocking, for the dog food came far closer to meeting ideal human needs.

I think it's altogether proper to put much of the blame for our inadequate national diet on those who do the shopping and cooking. But we should go deeper in seeking an answer. Shoppers, after all, are only reacting to the demands of their families and to the conditions they find in the stores. What has really happened is that the preparation of food has to a large extent been transferred from the kitchen to the food factories, and the consumer has become a middleman for the food industry. Instead of buying raw staple foods and blending them into meals in the kitchen, the home cook now takes orders from the rest of the family, who want the brand-name foods they see promoted on television and in newspapers and magazines. Then she or he builds an inventory of meals that have been selected, mixed, and often even cooked in factories. The result is that the family is not limited in its food selection by what the food preparer of the house can blend from raw materials. Its dietary choices are governed only by the family pocketbook. If Dad wants cake three or four times a day, it can be supplied to him because foods like that are now bought ready-made.

Anyone who shops in supermarkets can see the change that has come about in the way food is presented to the customer. But it has taken studies by the government and by first-rate scientists like Roger Williams to prove that all the glamour and superficial prettiness of packaged supermarket food is producing a poorer diet. Years ago when you went into a food store, you saw few foods in pretty boxes and packages but plenty of items close to the state in which they came off the farm. Even the smell was different. Instead of sniffing the disinfected, deodorized scent of the supermarket, you could feast your nostrils on the aroma of cured meats, raw soap, and ripening fruit in season.

The only trouble with food then was that it required plenty of work to get ready to eat. There were no instant foods. Coffee not only had to be percolated at home, it sometimes had to be roasted and ground, too. The food companies were on the right track when they took over the coffee-roasting and grinding chores, but they have gone too far beyond that in search of ways to do the consumer's work and turn a profit in the bargain. Food, like our environment, has become something to be exploited. The result is internal pollution. In addition to the chemicals put into food during processing, the internal pollution consists of an excess of food energy (calories) in relation to real food value (protein, vitamins, and minerals).

Unfortunately, once people get in a rut they have trouble getting out. Nobody likes eating chemical-laden food, but few have sufficient motivation to make the little extra effort to get better food. They don't realize how deep in the rut they are. They read the list of chemicals on a pack of processed food and those long names zip over their heads. They don't begin to understand what those chemicals are doing there in the food.

Even *my* eyes were opened by a look through some of the journals aimed at the people who are creating new kinds of food. Sporting names such as *Food Engineering, Food Product Development*, and *Food Technology*, they offer articles on such things as how to make imitation cheese and why people are eating so much ready-to-eat pudding. There are also articles on how to use food additives. In one issue there was an unintentionally funny story pointing out that real foods are so loaded with naturally occurring poisons that people can't be safe unless what they eat is made of chemicals. But the ads! On page after page, chemical companies let loose their trade secrets. They tell the people making new foods how to use chemicals to make more money by fooling people into thinking that the food coming out of envelopes and plastic packs is really better than (or at least as good as) the food that nature makes.

One recent article in *Food Engineering* was devoted to trumpeting the advent of yet another entirely artificial fruit drink. "There are many good synthetic orange drinks available, but have you seen a good natural-flavored version? One that need not contain a single drop of real orange juice?" "If not," crows the writer, fairly bursting with pride, "you'll have your chance next month when Continental Flavors of Brea, California, introduces its new 'Breakfast Orange Drink.' "

The treat in store promises to be rare indeed, for "the new product is really two new products—a combination clouding/stabilizing agent and a natural flavor WONF with artificial color (Yellow #5) added."

And if we crave something to eat between swallows of that dynamite orange brew, there's always a piece of the apple pie lovingly shown in a two-page close-up in *Food Product Development*. It isn't Mom's, of course, but a synthetic feast chock full of the not-so-goodies made by National Starch and Chemical Corporation.

We are told that with Baka-Snak "you can put a stop to post-bake shrinking of your crust." And "if you cook your fillings, Col-Flo 67 can make sure you have the right texture all the way to the table." Don't want to cook? Then "use Instant Clearjel for the same smooth texture."

And how about flavor? (Food processors worry a lot about flavor.) Well, we can relax, because National Starch and Chemical's "citrus crystals can add tartness to the taste of apple pie. N-Liven flavorings and Pure-Aid products enhance aroma, color, texture, and flavor in a variety of food products. And for special applications we have liquid and dry Capsul-Lok flavors to give you the essence of taste." Yum.

Many of the ads and articles in *Food Product Development* brag about the wonderful mouth-feel that will be created if food makers use this or that chemical. When these people start worrying about the feeling I get inside my mouth, I really get angry. Natural food is inherently pleasing to the mouth. Only when processing goes beyond the limits of good practices does your mouth tell you that something has gone wrong. The constant desire of the food tinkerers to add chemicals to mask that danger signal is a clear warning that they are going too far.

Another thing the food processors worry about too much is color. "No matter how nutritious, flavorful or well-textured a food is, it will never be eaten unless it is the right color," asserts another *Food Product Development* article. *Never* is a strong word for a scientific use, but the article's authors use it nonetheless. Chemical color is not essential to food marketing; it's a gimmick to fool people into thinking that something is fresh when it really is a bland imitation camouflaged with paints or powders. The deep orange cheese you like is usually white before processing. You would eat white cheese if that was the only kind you could get, but the food people figure orange turns the consumer on, and orange cheese is what's most easily available. You would also eat green oranges if you know that oranges can be both green and ripe at the same time, and if they were available. But again the food people have poured on the color.

What bothers me most is the feeling in the food trade that the old traditions are gone, that anything goes as long as people like the taste and can't tell the difference between what you are selling and real food.

You are what you eat. And the average American is eating food that is increasingly doctored with chemicals and decreasingly of any substantial nutritional value.

The best way to counter this assault on well-being is to grow as much of your food yourself as you possibly can. Most people find it difficult or impossible to grow all their own food, but almost anyone with access to a plot of land can grow some. That way, you know what you are putting into your soil and what is getting on your plants. You control all the processing steps and can use the food fresh.

When you buy food, plan and purchase carefully. Be suspicious of all convenience foods, because their convenience is purchased at a price higher than that on the package.

By switching to a diet rich in simple, hearty foods such as whole grains, beans, potatoes, nuts, and seeds, and in unprocessed vegetables, fruits, and animal-protein foods, you can get a full range of needed nutrients. Choosing these whole foods is a very positive form of diet change based on an appreciation of what is good and not on a fear of what is bad.

When you eat this kind of profoundly satisfying fare day after day, you will lose the craving for white flour and for highly sweetened drinks and desserts. It's important, though, to make an all-out effort to eat whole foods in as close to natural form as possible. Don't try to compromise by avoiding the worst commercial foods while still eating those which are less bad. Only really good foods can drive out the memory of the bad and free your taste buds from past conditioning.

Given our good farmland and favorable climate, wholesome foods only minimally processed could easily be produced and sold at reasonable prices to all Americans. But just as we are spoiling our natural soil fertility through industrialized farming practices, we are polluting the insides of our bodies with the wrong kinds of food.

Why Does Food Cost So Much?

We live in the country that is supposed to be the most efficient in the world, yet the price of food has been going up faster than the cost of many other things. This happens not just in the aftermath of poor growing seasons but even when there are record harvests. Why should that be? We have so much fertile land and a lot of big, wonderful machines to do much of the work. We should be eating the choicest foods at only nominal cost. But we aren't. The figure at the end of that long ticket from the supermarket keeps getting bigger all the time.

Can it be—a revolutionary thought indeed—that American farmers aren't really efficient? Few people would think to ask that question, taking for granted that anything as modern and mechanized as American farming must be efficient. Not everybody is so convinced, however. Michigan State University food scientist Georg Borgstrom has said that United States farmers are "robbing Peter to pay Paul" with methods that are using up resources at a faster rate than any other country's without achieving a correspondingly high state of efficiency. An extremely interesting article about Borgstrom's views was published in the *Michigan Farmer*. It pointed out that Borgstrom believes that American farmers are using energy resources—such as petroleum—in much greater amounts than is justified by the yields they produce.

Almost every farming operation uses energy and lots of it. In fact there was an 18 to 26 percent increase from 1979 to 1980 in the cost of raising a crop. Thirty-one percent of the energy used in food production in the United States is used in the manufacture of commercial nitrogen. That fertilizer energy is not always used in the wisest manner. For example, many farmers use large amounts of capital to purchase nitrogen in the form of fertilizer to grow corn. But fully 90 percent of the corn grown in this country is fed not directly to people but to livestock. And to get back one pound of edible protein in the form of meat, you must feed a steer 21.4 pounds of plant protein, a hog 8.2 pounds, and a chicken 5.5 pounds. Frances Moore Lappe, author of *Diet for a Small Planet*, has estimated that the feed cost of a single eight-ounce steak is the same as that for fifty cups of cooked cereal grains. Production of meat, for example, requires more energy expenditure, calorie for calorie, than production of sugar beets, the most efficient energy plant. (In an article in *Science*, David Pimentel and others calculated that if all the earth's petroleum reserves were used to produce an American-style meat-centered diet for everyone in the world, the world's oil would be gone in just thirteen years.)

Now it may appear that the United States can afford to squander so much of its energy on meat production. After all, when weather permits, our grain harvests continue to set new records. That seems to indicate that American agriculture is becoming more efficient. But is it really?

Georg Borgstrom has noted that until the 1930s, most American farmers produced crops without the aid of tractors. Horses were the form of power, and the feed used to keep them going was grown right on the farms. He figures that 66 million acres were used just to grow crops to feed draft animals. Now those animals are largely gone. Those 66 million acres are in food crop production, and farmers are buying petroleum, gas, and electricity to meet their energy needs. "It's no wonder we have surplus," he says. It is his view that the surplus doesn't prove the efficiency of the American farmer, just that he is blessed at the moment with the means to use up energy resources at a rapid rate. All the easily available energy resources and land are being consumed in one generation. "What," asks Borgstrom, "will the next generation do?"

The standard way to justify the efficiency rate of the American farmer is to point out how many more people he is now feeding. Back in 1900 each farmer fed only five persons besides himself. Today each farmer produces enough to feed about seventy other people. Although that comparison appears to speak very convincingly for farm efficiency, it only intensifies our wonderment over the rapidly increasing cost of food in the stores. If the overall efficiency of our food production establishment were increasing, food prices would be getting lower all the time; but they are not.

"You can't compare a farmer of 1900 with a farmer today," Borgstrom says. "They are not the same kind of animal. In 1900 he butchered animals, delivered milk and meat to the cities, churned butter, salted meat, made sausages, farmed with horses for which he produced his own feed, made his own machines, baked bread, made all his own repairs and built his own buildings."

Times have changed considerably since then, and today these things are being done by outside industries. Borgstrom calculates that if you add the number of people performing such support services for farmers to the number of farmers, then "divide this number into the . . . population, you can see it takes in relative terms nearly the same number of people to feed America today as it did in 1900."

Efficiency in food production also must be judged in terms of the amount of soil fertility resources that are being consumed. The large amounts of energy we are applying to the growing of crops are not creating a balanced system of farming on all of our lands. Minerals and organic matter are being depleted in many places. Soil tilth and structure is being pounded by heavy machinery, creating hardpans. Erosion of topsoil continues in many areas. Ancient reserves of water are being used up in dry places like California and Texas.

Our new awareness of the cost of pollution is also directing attention to the hidden price tag on food produced through the use of chemicals we now know are poisoning our land, our water, and the crops themselves. Although food already seems expensive when you buy it in the store, its price in terms of assaults on our environment and health is much greater than the total you pay the supermarket clerk. Efforts to control pollution, increase water supplies, and pay for farm subsidies also are reflected in our taxes and make the cost of eating even higher.

Because of the prevailing belief that what we are doing is right economically, few people have tried to take an objective look at the real cost of producing food and the reasons why the cost is so high. But with world population growing rapidly and the need for food increasing at the same rate, it is necessary to know not only whether we are getting a food bargain at home, but also whether our ideas and methods are sound enough to pass along to the rest of the world. If you look beneath the propaganda, it appears that we in America still have not found all the answers to the economical production of food.

Food Power

Sadly, much of the damage to our grocery budgets has been self-inflicted. The great majority of people has been all too willing to allow the basic nature of their food to be changed by processing, without complaining or even wondering about the long-term effect. Convenience was the promise. Why cook food at home when it can be prepared for you somewhere else? Why peel potatoes, squeeze oranges, slice bread, wait for oatmeal to cook, bake your own beans, or make soup? Most people were happy to have those jobs done in food factories and felt that the small extra cost was acceptable. Food was cheap anyway, wasn't it? The extra cost for processing seemed a bargain when you considered the convenience.

Only now can everyone see clearly how much those minutes of freedom from food preparation cost. A few potato peels here and there have added up to vast potato dehydrating factories, located far from markets and creating the need for colored cardboard boxes, many trucks, warehouses, advertising, and other expenses. The small, local potato farms passed away. Every type of convenience food has had a similar effect. Small farms, supplying nearby markets with basic commodities, were replaced by vast factory-farms, tied directly to processing plants, which turned rustic foods into glamorized and very expensive meal ingredients.

But as prices went up, nutrient value was processed away and questionable additives took its place. Take potatoes, for example. According to figures compiled for 1971–1977, one-half of all American potatoes are now being dehydrated or otherwise processed. They are peeled, stripped of their moisture, their vitamin C, and their protein, larded with chemical preservatives, packaged in fancy boxes, and then stored until they find their way into the American kitchen. All that processing is being justified in the name of convenience for the American consumers. While the farmer is not benefiting from the processing of potatoes as much as the food companies, for some strange reason the farmer's government spokesman, the U.S. Department of Agriculture, is pushing the idea with everything it has.

The USDA believes that processing of potatoes is the solution to the potato marketing problem. The department's magazine, *Agricultural Research*, ran an article several years back strongly plugging processed potatoes, but some of the article's information was simply not correct. "In nutritive value, processed and fresh potatoes were basically similar," it said. "Dishes prepared from dehydrated mixes, including au gratin, scalloped and hash-browned potatoes and potato soup, had higher carbohydrate and mineral content and lower protein content than fresh potatoes. This difference is not critical because potatoes are not a major source of protein in U.S. diets."

First it says that the nutritive value of processed and fresh potatoes is similar, then it concludes that the differences are not critical because nobody eats potatoes for their protein content. That is typical Washington double-talk. Conveniently forgotten or deliberately ignored is the significant vitamin C content of potatoes, which is depleted by two-thirds when potatoes are dehydrated. The USDA forgot that fact in its enthusiastic plug for processing, even though potatoes are a very important source of vitamin C in the American diet.

But vanishing vitamins and minerals and an onslaught of

additives are only the beginning of the problem. A continuous stream of new evidence is showing that processed food strikes much deeper at our health and security.

There is also a rapidly growing body of evidence that the removal of nonnutritive fiber from food during processing is an important cause of a wide variety of diseases, ranging from cancer of the colon and appendicitis to overweight and heart attack. The diets of primitive peoples are usually loaded with nonnutritive fiber, such as bran from wheat and other fiber from beans, nuts, fruits, vegetables, and seed foods in general. That fiber gives the gut something to do, exercises it and keeps it fit, allays hunger pangs, prevents constipation, and keeps our digestive processes in tune. Most important of all, according to latest findings, fiber in the diet works in the intestinal tract to "bind" bile salts which are produced from cholesterol. What this means is that the body makes more bile salts from stored reserves of cholesterol. The result is a significant lowering of cholesterol in the blood.

The need to increase fiber in the American diet to prevent chronic disease has become widely recognized. What hasn't been explored, though, is how important the removal and dilution of fiber is to the health of the food processing industries. In the majority of all convenience foods, from sliced bread and frozen dinners to fruit juice and jams, natural foods go into the factories with adequate fiber and come out with the fiber either stripped or diluted through the addition of sugar and other fiberless food ingredients.

Why is that done? Consumer preference for smooth, bland, sweetened foods is part of the story. But the main reason is that nonnutritive fiber is just not compatible with the whole mystique and the business realities of processed food. It's too cheap. Too rustic. Too bland in flavor, too lacking in glamour to fit in with the hard-sell food business system that translates into big profits. Even the health food stores have trouble getting and selling that premier fiber food, bran, because it is cheap, bulky, and holds little profit for shippers.

Food processing also has upset the relationship among the natural and necessary elements in foods. Take salt for example. Cultural historians surmise that salt (sodium chloride) consumption probably dates back to biblical times. For a long time, then, salt has been the "sacred cow" of the table. The consumption of salt by our ancestors was often alarmingly high, but nothing in comparison to what most people consume today. Why the change in salt habits? The primary reason is that sodium chloride is added to many foods during processing to maintain color and flavor, as well as for its preservative properties.

Let's get specific. An edible portion (100 grams) of raw green garden peas contains approximately 2 milligrams of sodium. But when the same peas are commercially canned, the sodium content jumps to 236 milligrams. This tremendous increase in sodium content is only half the problem. An increase in the sodium content means that there will be a profound decrease in potassium. The same edible portion of peas has 316 milligrams of potassium when raw and 96 milligrams when canned (processed).

According to George R. Meneely, M.D., writing in *Qualitas Plantarum*, "Naturally occurring dietary potassium has protected against human addition of excessive sodium chloride." Unfortunately, the massive amount of sodium added by food processors has upset this delicate natural balance. Furthermore, indications are that this high-sodium, low-potassium state contributes to hypertension, kidney disease, and urinary complaints.

Dr. Meneely estimates that people need no more than one gram of salt a day. Since close to 1 percent of an edible portion (100 grams) of any kind of processed food is salt, we can guess that most people consume far more salt than their bodies need. Instead of throwing salt over their shoulders, too many Americans throw it on their food. And the unhappy result is the unconscious addiction to many processed foods.

Another ingredient used to "amp up" the flavor of engineered foods is sugar. Sugar is the processor's number one ally and our number one foe. Without announcing the practice to shoppers, food processors have been gradually slipping more and more of this sweet nothing into our foods. Approximately 65 percent of the refined sugar produced today is consumed by the food and beverage industry while only 24 percent is going for home use. In no uncertain terms, many Americans are hooked on the stuff.

In *Psychodietics*, Drs. Emanuel Cheraskin and Marshall Ringsdorf write that "refined sugar is not only valueless, but a chemical menace, for it lacks the very B vitamins and minerals necessary for assimilation." Excessive sugar consumption (and this is the fate of anyone who eats primarily processed foods) has been linked to hypoglycemia (low blood sugar), an ailment characterized by irrational behavior, emotional instability, and distorted judgment.

Evidence mounts daily that the physical act of the processing of food—especially the elimination of fiber and the addition of salt and sugar—presents real and immediate hazards. While as consumers and health-minded individuals we may not be able to control prices, we do hold the power of the purse—food power.

Time is running out. Processing is becoming more pervasive and more perilous. If we were still in an affluent society, were enjoying excellent health, and lived in a world free from hunger, we would be justified in thinking our food-processing establishment a real asset and convenience. But things aren't going well. Money is hard to come by, and processed food is more expensive. It is increasingly seen as the cause of many health problems.

If we are serious about wanting better health, our only alternative is to switch from factory-processed food to more fresh vegetables and fruits, whole grains, beans, and similar foods.

Our Daily Meat

Recommending meat is not a fashionable thing for a health writer to do these days. Vegetarianism is in. People who are not total vegetarians are telling their friends that they don't eat as much red meat as they used to. There is worry about the fat in meat and the growth-stimulating drugs that are used to fatten farm animals. The cost of meat is going up rapidly, pricing the more glamorous part of animals out of reach of the average person. Just one of those negatives can turn a person off to steak, or even hamburger, but taken together they form an ever-stronger "meat is bad" impression in the public's mind.

I have been eating less meat myself for the past few years. Two things have caused me to do that. One is the desire to have a low-fat diet. And the other is the recent stream of experimental studies showing that grains (especially whole grains), beans, and vegetables have strong health-building values as well as tremendous disease-prevention power. Not only are those foods rich in fiber, but they have other health benefits as well.

Vegetarianism is not for me, though. I will cut down on meat but not eliminate it from my diet. Part of the reason is that being a vegetarian involves hassles that don't appeal to me. I wouldn't be comfortable asking my friends for special foods when eating at their houses, and I wouldn't want to eat only restaurant vegetables when I travel. But there are deeper, more meaningful reasons why I don't change a lifelong habit. Certain food values in meat are hard to find in most foods. At least one vitamin—B_{12}—falls into that category. But that is only the beginning. Meat has protein of superb quality. It is also a rich source of minerals that are tough to get in other foods. And I would be willing to bet that there are still undiscovered nutritional factors in meat that give nonvegetarians an extra share of health and good feeling.

You have to realize that our relationship with animals as food-providers is a very old and natural thing. We have been partners-in-survival for a very long time. People and animals literally grew up together. That relationship has, I feel, imprinted on us a basic need to rely on animals to give us the food values we must have to live at top form. Birds and animals have a way of offering us good things, and I feel that we human beings still have great potential for merging our activities successfully with those of animals. I would even go so far as to say that the natural cycles and rhythms of life which sustain us would be broken if we took a "people only" point of view and didn't relate to domestic animals in proper ways.

Keep in mind that animals don't have to compete with us for food. When kept as part of an organic homestead or small farm system, birds and animals often use pasture areas that are unsuitable for regular farming. They eat types of things that simply aren't palatable to us. We don't have the multiple stomachs of ruminant animals that allow them to graze on a variety of grasses and other plants. That's important for two reasons. Those plants we can't eat—but which animals can—may contain some minerals we need. Perhaps more important, the ability of grazing animals to eat all the plants we can't digest creates an extra amount of food for us. Regular crops like corn and wheat often can't be grown on steep hillsides, dry plains, and low, marshy meadows. But those places do grow plants on which animals graze. In this increasingly overpopulated world, we need desperately the food that can be produced in that way.

For even greater efficiency in converting otherwise unwanted vegetable matter into food when space is limited, we probably should consider using goats more and perhaps breeding small strains of other livestock. In India, for example, there are many cows which have been bred to miniature size for a special purpose. They are used to pull plows and harrows in some rice paddies that are so soft that large cows and bullocks would sink in and get stuck. Maybe these small cows would be interesting to American homesteaders who want to keep a cow or two but don't need the large amount of milk and meat that a standard-sized animal produces. Perhaps some of these small Indian cows could be brought here. Or perhaps the already-diminutive Jersey could be bred even smaller.

I predict that by the end of this century rabbit could be one of the most common types of meat sold in stores. It will also be a popular item on restaurant menus. For one thing, the meat of domestic rabbit is much like that of its wild relatives—at least in the quality of its fat. Rabbit meat contains mainly unsaturated fat. It's also low in cholesterol and sodium and contains no additives. Those are important qualities, and as they become more widely known, the popularity of rabbit is bound to increase.

Rabbits can thrive on a high-roughage diet, eating things like hay, grass clippings, vegetable wastes, and a variety of abundant plants. They generally grow faster when fed grain as well, but grain doesn't have to be their total diet, as is the case with chickens. Researchers working on Rodale Press's Cornucopia Project forecast big increases in the cost of grain in coming years, so an animal like the rabbit that can grow well on little or no grain is likely to become much less expensive to produce than other types of meat. Beef animals also can live on a high-roughage diet, eating hay and pasture grasses, but rabbits produce five times more meat per pound of such food than do steers.

Just as we are turning now to compact cars for transportation, we'll be buying more compact and efficient animals for our future dinners. Look for rabbit next time you go to market, and give it a try. Maybe you'll agree that it is the kind of meat that helps you feel good, both nutritionally and economically.

In addition to preventing the waste of some of our best resources, animals are also good recyclers. Many Chinese families keep chickens, and they don't buy feed for them. The birds eat leftovers from the table, plus whatever insects, worms, and bits of grass they can forage. An American family, with a far larger output of garbage and a large yard, would have no trouble at all keeping a fair-sized flock of chickens. Of course, you can also put table scraps in your compost pile, but having your own source of eggs is very comforting.

Animals are a continuous, living food-storage system—a hedge against hard times or a sudden need for extra food. Vegetables and fruits usually have to be either eaten or processed when they are ready to be picked, but animals can be "stored" alive for months or even years. Having a cellar full of canned and dried food gives you a good feeling, but knowing that you have a flock or herd to cull from is just as good, maybe even better.

Remember also that animals do more for us than just supply meat. I spoke not long ago with a part-time farmer who has made a business of selling high-grade wool from his flock of sheep. He has learned how to care for the sheep and their wool properly, and has developed a list of handweavers who pay double the going rate for his wool because it is so clean and long-fibered. People wait a year or more to buy some of that wool.

Without animals, we wouldn't have hides or leather. Or milk, cheese, and yogurt. We wouldn't have eggs or feather pillows either. There would be no bone meal for us to use as a calcium supplement, and no natural bristles for our brushes. Perhaps most important of all, in a world without animals we would soon run out of animal manure.

Would that be a bad thing? Most certainly! Manure is the high-nitrogen, mineral-rich catalyst that puts spark back into the earth better than any fertilizer. Without manure, compost-making and soil-building would be a difficult struggle. With manure, renewing the soil's fertility each year becomes practical and efficient—part of a simple recycling system.

Animals also give us some very important psychological values. They help to connect us to a community belonging to the land. I felt that deeply during my growing-up, when our family kept chickens, goats, cattle, and horses. It fell to me to do much of the work of feeding the animals and cleaning the stables, which often was very hard labor and required getting up early on cold mornings, plus finding a substitute if I couldn't do the job for a day or two.

That experience set my life in a regular pattern, and also taught me to be aware of the welfare of others. True, most of the animals I was caring for were going to be killed, but while they were alive I was responsible for all their needs. They had no one to turn to but me for the things I was giving them, and my young mind was impressed by that responsibility.

Perhaps the greatest value of animals, though, is that they serve as a reflection of ourselves and our society. Look at the chicken to see what I mean. A thousand or so years ago chickens were lean, tough, independent. They scratched for their own living around human settlements. Those chickens that couldn't fly out of danger didn't live very long. The principle of survival of the fittest kept the breed light, mobile, and able to defend itself.

Today, the chicken is a changed bird. The change started when people began selecting for breeding only those birds which matured quickly, laid the most eggs, grew the fattest, and weren't inclined to fly away. Thus helped, chickens were transformed from semiwild camp followers to soft, plump egg-laying champions.

By remaking the chicken we have gained some advantages. Eggs and chicken meat have become cheap food, available everywhere. The shells of the eggs have been made white, because most people like that symbol of purity. The advantages stop there, and disadvantages begin.

The taste of chicken meat has eroded into a pale imitation of its former golden flavor. And as much of the old chicken taste has been lost, so has our cultural partnership with chickens faded. The crowing of cocks no longer amuses and awakens farm and city people alike. Roosters are hardly needed at all these days, especially by hens who live in cage-wire apartments with fewer amenities than maximum-security prisons. Food is delivered by conveyor, and the daily egg rolls quietly away on a special track, to be cracked by a machine instead of human hands.

Has not our own society followed the same path as the changed world of the chickens? More homes have become compartmentalized high-rises. Food is more synthetic. Less physical work is needed. Those different conditions of life have changed us. Like today's chickens, we are now softer, weaker, and more lonely. In the short run we are secure, but our long-run welfare is clouded by the complex systems needed for our support. Neither modern chickens nor people could long survive a breakdown in the central flow of energy.

Cattle, too, are no longer lean, independent, and healthy animals feeding on an open range. They mature in crowded feedlots and are routinely dosed with antibiotics and growth hormones to promote fast weight gain. Indeed, even though diethylstilbesterol (DES) was outlawed in 1979, feedlot operators continue to use it illegally. Currently, the U.S. Department of Agriculture lacks the authority to quarantine or confiscate sample animals tested on a producer's farm if they are found to be tainted. The USDA can only confiscate tainted meat at the meat packing plant. But many producers manage to sell their contaminated cattle to unsuspecting slaughterhouses and meat known to be tainted is passed on to the consumer.

Our meat is also being degraded by the chemicals used in processing it. Much of the bacon, ham, hot dogs, sausage, and luncheon meat on American tables has been treated with *sodium nitrite,* a curing agent shown to be carcinogenic in a three-year study done at the Massachusetts Institute of Technology.

Unfortunately, the Food and Drug Administration has not responded to the bad news about nitrite by taking products made with it off the market. Nor has it required that such meats be prepared without nitrites, which is quite possible and has been done for years by small meat packers. The FDA has said that banning nitrites would disrupt the food system, as well as create the possibility (which I feel is very slight) that untreated meats would allow the botulism organism to grow. Yet that has been an extremely rare occurrence, and nitrite-free meats have been sold for a long time.

Recent evidence suggests that supplementary amounts of vitamin C can keep the nitrites in meat from being converted inside the body to nitrosamine, which has been linked to the development of bowel cancer. In fact, researchers have found that several grams of vitamin C a day can reduce and sometimes even get rid of polyps in the large intestine. (These growths sometimes precede colon cancer.)

But why should we have to rely on self-care to protect ourselves from chemicals that don't belong in meat in the first place? An alternative, of course, is to avoid all processed meats. It's a good idea to do this anyway because they are loaded with salt and saturated fat, two contributors to high blood pressure and heart disease. If possible, try to seek out organically grown meat, which is completely free of chemicals and drugs now in standard use by most farmers and commercial meat producers, or eat more wild meat.

The meat of wild animals is the most nutritious. There are at least three reasons why that is so. First, wild animals graze over a larger area than do farm animals, which often are fed just on a few kinds of grain. The varied diet of animals in the wild gives them a better chance to present us with a balance of the very important but sometimes hard to get trace minerals.

Wild animals also aren't fed antibiotics and other drugs to make them gain weight faster. They aren't fed potent chemicals which flow throughout their systems and kill flies and other bugs which bother them. Some people with extreme allergies to synthetic chemicals eat only wild animal meat in order to get the pure diet they need to stay healthy.

The most healthful thing about wild animal meat, though, is its low fat content. Wild creatures are lean. They fend for themselves, and are designed by nature to be efficient, strong, and able to live without those generous and fattening handouts of corn that farm animals have thrust on them. If you could look at the meat of a wild pig, for example, you'd see that it is almost totally lean. The globs of fat that surround the muscle meat of farm pigs are nowhere to be seen. The meat of a deer compares to beef in the same way. A venison roast is almost all muscle, while a beef roast is larded with fat. Recently, the public's taste has turned toward beef and pork that is less fatty, but the meat of wild animals is still dramatically lean by comparison.

Perhaps the best health idea of all is to eat meat—especially beef—less often. Here is why. Like that of chickens and pigs, the inner nature of beef cattle has been altered by genetic manipulation, and the result for the human community may be far-reaching. For while we human beings have not been selectively bred, and have remained very close to our wild and uncivilized ancestors in structure, we inhabit a world populated with grossly inflated and fatty farm animals.

British biochemist M. A. Crawford believes that domestication of the cow has changed drastically the kind of fat present in the meat and that the change may be a prime contributing factor in the prevalence of heart disease in industrialized countries today. Dr. Crawford found that domestic cows have much more fat in their meat than the wild animals to which they are closely related. Even more important, he found that the composition of the fat of each type of animal was very different. In what he calls the "free-living" wild animals, polyunsaturated fatty acids made up about 30 percent of the fat total—a considerable amount. In the domestic cows, only 2 percent of the fat was polyunsaturated.

Animal fats with their high content of saturated fatty acids have been shown clearly to be part of a diet which may lead to coronary artery disease. But Dr. Crawford thinks we should be a little more specific and think of what he calls "domestic fat" as dangerous to the heart. Wild bovine animals not forced to eat the typical fattening ration for beef and dairy animals have a much healthier fat and should not be incriminated along with domestic animals.

As statistical proof of his theory, Dr. Crawford explains that human beings have been on this earth for at least a million years, and we have domesticated animals for approximately ten thousand years. But only in the last few generations have we given our domestic animals a much different diet than they had when they were wild. Previously, cows grazed on whatever pasture was available and weren't fed fattening rations of concentrated food. Animal fat simply wasn't available in the vast quantities that are eaten today. What animal fat was available was largely of the polyunsaturated type. It's easy to see that if Dr. Crawford's conclusions are right, our modern animals have indeed been killing us through their imbalanced type of fat.

I believe it is right for us to eat some meat, because human beings have always eaten meat. Our absolute need for vitamin B_{12}, for which meat is an important source, is good evidence of that. We also know that primitive people ate small and large animals whenever they could get them. But should we eat prime ribs of beef from an animal that has been changed genetically to produce vast amounts of fat? Should we eat hot dogs loaded with the fat of modern pigs? No. Those are not natural foods. A beefsteak marbled with fat is not a natural food. A fatty ham is not a natural food.

To those who understand what natural food really is, my advice is to eat occasional small portions of modern meat, avoiding the fat as much as possible. Skip the skin on chicken, for example, and eat just the white meat. Plan many meals which don't include meat at all.

Remember that liver is loaded with good nutrients. Liver is literally a vitamin and mineral supplement that you eat with a knife and fork instead of taking in pill form. If you don't care for the taste of liver, or if you can't get it often enough, you can add desiccated liver tablets to your supplement list. Desiccated liver is one of the oldest of all the natural food supplements and is still very popular.

When looking over the meat case at your supermarket,

Fat Content of Selected Meats

Meat Cut*	% Fat	% Saturated	% Unsaturated
Beef			
chuck	9.4	48	46
flank steak	7.2	48	46
ground beef (lean)	11.2	48	46
porterhouse	10.4	48	46
sirloin	7.6	48	46
round steak	6.1	48	46
rump roast	9.2	48	47
Chicken			
dark meat	6.3	32	58
light meat	3.4	31	58
Duck, domesticated	4.2	37	46
Lamb			
leg	7.0	57	40
loin chops	7.4	56	39
Rabbit	10.1	38	49
Turkey			
dark meat	8.3	28	63
light meat	3.9	30	64

SOURCES: *Composition of Foods: Poultry Products: Raw, Processed, Prepared,* United States Department of Agriculture Handbook 8–5, 1979.

Nutritive Value of American Foods in Common Units, United States Department of Agriculture Handbook 456, 1975.

Unpublished data, Consumer Nutrition Center, Science and Education Administration, United States Department of Agriculture.

NOTES: Rabbit, while high in overall fat, is very low in saturated fat, the kind that may hurt your heart. On the other hand, even beef cuts that are somewhat low in fat are highly saturated.

Since meats contain several other types of fats as well as the saturated and unsaturated ones, the totals do not equal 100 percent.

*All are trimmed of excess fat or skin after cooking.

search out the types of meat with less visible fat. The eye of the round is the lowest in fat of all beef cuts, but that can be expensive. Round steak, bottom round, and rump roasts are lower in fat, too, and less costly. You'll have to cook these low-fat cuts longer and may need to apply more imagination to their preparation. But the payoff in health and good nutrition will be more than worth the extra time and effort.

The Whole Meaning of *Natural*

ne word! All the truths about nutrition that you'll ever need to know to plan a good diet are inside one word. But to get those truths out and put them to use you need to know more than the identity of the word itself. You have to peel away the outer layers of confusion to get at its inner meaning.

Then, after you have penetrated the central core of that word, you can deal directly with fundamental concepts of nutrition. You become as good an authority on what is good to eat and what isn't as anyone else—including the Ph.D. nutritionists. Whole diet plans, or lists of individual foods, can be evaluated easily. Suddenly you will see clearly why bad diets are no good, and what makes them that way. And good ways of eating will become etched more firmly into your mind, because you'll know why they are good.

Natural is the word. I am convinced that as long as we eat natural foods, we are going to have the best possible chance of maintaining our health through a long and nutritionally happy life. But what are natural foods? Are they foods which are fresh, unrefined, and minimally processed? Are natural foods all those foods which don't contain artificial additives? Or is there some deeper meaning of the word *natural* that we must understand?

Yes, there is that deeper meaning. The word *natural* on a jar of peanut butter or a package of cereal merely hints at it. What we really need to know is whether a certain kind of food is natural for us to eat. Our understanding of the word *natural* must encompass ourselves as well as our food. We need to know our own nature—what we ourselves are, in a physical sense. Because our nature, as physical beings, is fixed. We can't change what we are, so we must feed ourselves the things that fit naturally into our system.

Let's ramble back in time in search of the complete definition of *natural*. In fact, if we go back a million years, there's no indication that our body's digestive system was any different than it is now. About forty thousand years ago, our bodies were physically the same as they are now. Of course, if we were alive then, our clothes would look different. We would live in caves or huts instead of houses or apartments. There would be no modern conveniences. What is especially important is that our food would be different. It would be all wild. There was no farming then. Everything people ate was collected from nature.

Think about that for a moment. We are living today in bodies that are not modern and that are in no way adapted to handling synthetic compounds or artificial foods. Although our minds are tuned to the ways of a modern age, we are living in bodies that are adapted to a primitive diet. Here is a sample menu from that time: various kinds of nuts, seeds, berries, and leaves were mixed together into a porridge. Think of all the fiber that food contained. Fruit was a common item of diet. But it was more nutritious than most of today's fruit because it was freshly picked. Again, it was rich in fiber. Salt was hard to get, so sodium in that primitive diet came mostly from the naturally occurring salts in food and water. Fat was a rarity, because wild animals don't carry around the masses of lard and suet that modern animals produce. The only sweetener available was honey, and that was a rare treat.

That old-time diet was not lush and rich like much modern food. Often there were shortages of food. But that authentically natural diet worked. It supported a human society which gradually increased in number for millions of years. We are biochemically like those early, "primitive" people, but collectively we're not nearly as smart as they were in searching for and selecting food.

Many of the nutrition-related problems of today are caused by the fact that our primitive inner selves simply aren't able to absorb in a healthful way the modern foods that our minds think we should be able to eat. It is our nature to eat foods which have a close relationship to the kinds of wild foods our ancestors gathered. And understanding our nature also helps us understand what natural food really is. The two go together.

Given the immense changes in our food supply that have happened over the past century, there is a great need to have a clearer picture in our heads of what natural food is. We see the word thrust at us so often on packaged-food labels. The word *natural* sells, so it is put on almost anything that doesn't contain chemical additives (and maybe even on the labels of a few foods that do). The idea of natural food, its real value in preserving our health, is too important to be lost in a jungle of advertising claims.

Of course, I'm happy to see the word *natural* used on food labels when it is used truthfully. I'm especially happy about the fact that the label "natural" not only promotes good food, but also advertises that most food sold in stores is not natural, is refined too much, and is too laden with additives. Many of the processed food companies are defensive about that. They've even started using TV commercials to counter the growing trend toward respect for natural foods, using clever advertising concepts to twist consumer perceptions of which kind of food is really better. Another prong of that antinatural promotion campaign is the growing number of newspaper and magazine articles by scientists pointing out that there are many toxins in natural foods.

Here again, knowing the truth about our own nature and about our inner history puts that kind of talk in perspective. Sure, there are plenty of plants which produce poisons. And they range in toxicity from being mildly nonnutritive—like some of the inhibitors in beans and other seeds that are rendered inactive by heat—to the most toxic kinds of poisons imaginable. We need to realize that plants are not put on this earth entirely for our benefit. They serve other functions as well.

We can find out what those natural toxins are, though, and either avoid or neutralize them. Our ancestors of many centuries ago did that quite successfully by a process of trial and error. They discovered which plants and other foods made them sick, then stopped using them. Knowledge about which were good and which weren't so good was then passed down from one generation to another. Today, with modern analytical methods, we can find out much more about naturally occurring toxins and can protect ourselves from them more effectively. I see them as just one more good reason why we need to relate our nature to the nature of our food. Natural food must be good for us in all ways, and not just something that falls within the bounds of a definition limiting the kind of processing that is permissible.

There is another vital point to be made about natural toxins. Being created in a natural environment, they also are programmed to degrade and decay in a natural environment. If you collect a potful of poisonous berries and then put them in a compost heap to rot, they are usually decomposed into harmless humus. So we don't have to fear any generalized poisoning of the environment by plants. In contrast, a wide range of synthetic chemicals doesn't decay or degrade. Or they disappear very slowly, and can even accumulate as higher concentrations in the food chain and the human body.

Of course, I realize that times have changed. We no longer hunt for and gather our food. Many of the wild kinds of food our bodies have been created to function best on can't be bought in stores. Junk food is thrust at us from all directions. In such a confusing atmosphere, how can we begin to make intelligent choices that will lead us to a way of living that is more natural for us? You can make an important start toward living with your history just by cutting way back on salt. In fact, the story of the human need and desire for salt provides an almost perfect example of how important and inflexible our inner program is.

For the great bulk of human history, getting enough salt was a major challenge. True, there is plenty of salt in the oceans and getting it out is not difficult. But most primitive people didn't live near oceans and had no easy way to get salt from water or from underground mines. So as our human inner system developed and evolved, we became tuned to need a very small amount—about ½ gram. Without that bit of salt each day, the body will automatically excrete fluids to try to keep the inner salt content in balance. In an extreme lack of salt, the body will literally dry up.

Animals have the same need for salt as we do, so when primitive people ate a diet made up largely of their flesh, they did not have to worry about getting extra salt. People who lived largely on plants, though, needed extra salt to meet their requirement. Some primitive people burned plants and ate the ashes to increase their salt intake. Others, like the Masai in Africa, drank the blood and urine of cows to satisfy their salt hunger.

As civilization advanced, the salt situation changed drastically. After evolving bodies adjusted to function well on the small amount of salt in a totally natural diet, people began using salt to preserve meat and to pickle and ferment vegetables so they could be stored. The average salt intake increased dramatically, out of necessity and also because people able to get large amounts of salt found that they enjoyed the flavor it added to foods.

The use of salt in America and other advanced countries today far exceeds our actual requirement. Typical daily intakes range from seven to fifteen grams per person, with some people consuming as much as thirty grams. Those are not figures I have picked out of the air. They are based on careful studies of the quantities of salt consumed by typical people. Nutritionist Jean Mayer has said that "the average American eats about 10 times as much salt as his body needs."

Why is so much salt used? There are two reasons. The first and more obvious one is that many people have become adjusted (you might even say addicted) to the taste of salt in food and drinks. They could have gained that taste addiction when they were tiny babies, from processed infant food that was salted to make it taste good to their mothers. Salting food heavily is also a cultural addiction. If you see your parents or friends covering their food with a dusting of salt from a shaker, you tend to do likewise.

The second reason is that salt is put in almost every processed food. Go through your pantry reading labels on food packages and see what I mean. Sardines are salted. Mustard is salted. Soup is salted. Bread is salted. Olives are loaded with salt. So are cheese, processed meat, soy sauce, and just about every other packaged food you can buy.

How can we get away with that kind of salt abuse of our inner historical program? The answer is simple. Many people can survive a salty diet in the short run, but not in the long run. Our bodies have a natural mechanism for dumping excess salt on a day-to-day basis. Eat salt and you'll drink more water, and urinate more. The inner balancing mechanism of the body (homeostasis) will keep your blood salt level stable at an ideal amount but to do that you'll have to flush more water through your system to keep that salt moving out.

There remains a very serious health problem caused by salt eating, though. The amount of fluid retained between human cells is increased by even moderate salt use. Called extracellular fluid, that liquid increases body weight but has a far more important effect as well. Larger amounts of extracellular fluid force the heart to work harder pushing blood through the kidneys' filtering system. That effort could result in essential hypertension, or high blood pressure—one of the most serious health problems of this age.

The connection between salt use and high blood pressure has been suspected for over seventy years. In recent years, evidence implicating salt in this enormous health problem has accumulated from so many sources that an almost overwhelming case for the salt-hypertension hypothesis has been made.

Studies of the salt-use habits of primitive tribes have yielded very productive information. Dozens of investigators have traveled to remote regions of the world, taking blood pressure readings of primitive peoples and comparing that information with their salt-use habits. They've also looked carefully at other health and lifestyle factors which could cause high blood pressure.

According to an article by Edward D. Freis, M.D., which was published in the journal *Circulation,* in just about every case, primitive people who have access to salt and use it as a condiment and food preservative have high blood pressure problems. Those people who still live the way people have been conditioned to live by their inner historical programs—that is, with only tiny amounts of salt—have almost no high blood pressure.

Another observer, F. W. Lowenstein, went into the Brazilian jungle and looked at the health of two tribes living near each other. People in the Mundurucus tribe had been converted to Christianity by missionaries and were introduced to salt. Even though the Mundurucus still lived very primitively in other respects, the blood pressure of the people tended to rise, especially as they got older.

Nearby lived the Carajas tribe, which had had no contact at all with civilization and used no table salt. The blood pressure of the Carajas people did not rise as they got older. They had no hypertension at all. Similar results have been found among primitive people living in the Solomon Islands, New Guinea, Malaysia, Uganda, and the Kalahari Desert of Africa.

Although the evidence of salt's effect on the health of primitive people is very clear, tracking salt use among Americans and relating that to high blood pressure problems has produced somewhat conflicting results. Many people "give up" salt, but their high blood pressure remains a difficulty. They remain stuck on a regimen of antihypertension drugs that must be continued for the rest of their lives.

The root of the problem is that salt is so pervasive in our food, drink, and even drugs that getting salt intake down to a level that will reverse a tendency toward high blood pressure requires careful thought and planning. Many doctors have advised their patients merely to "stop using the saltshaker," thinking that puts them on a low-salt diet. How wrong they are!

Dr. Freis points out in his special article on salt that people must reduce their salt intake to about one gram "to produce more than a minimal reduction of blood pressure." That's possible if a person stays away from all processed foods and avoids using the saltshaker as well. Small amounts of salt occur naturally in meat, eggs, and even vegetables. If you eat fresh meats, eggs, vegetables, and grains that you know have not been salted, you can keep within that one gram (1,000 milligrams) level. But start making exceptions for processed foods and right away you'll go near or over the limit.

Obviously, just by trying not to eat salt you'll be guided away from foods that go against your basic nature. Another helpful rule of thumb is to be wary of most fat-rich foods. Only lately has a dairy industry developed which is able to produce large quantities of fat-rich products. So it is clear to me that we are upsetting the harmony of our inner system by eating large amounts of butter, ice cream, rich cheese, fatty meat, and similar foods that supply too much fat, cholesterol, and calories in relation to their good nutrients. The fact that those foods can be called natural doesn't make them better for us.

Another good rule is to go easy on sweet foods. Sugar is as far from the natural, fibrous starchiness of most wild grains and vegetables as you can get. Honey is only natural for you to eat if you consume it as often as our primitive ancestors were likely to, which was very seldom indeed.

Replace fatty, salty, or sweet foods with those more in keeping with your inner nature. Eat some bran every day. If you are allergic to wheat, as some are, eat corn or soy bran. Bran is a primitive but packaged food which puts some of the best qualities of a truly wild and natural diet into our meals. Try to get fiber from vegetables, seeds, and nuts as well. Don't forget to emphasize whole grains in your diet, too. They are natural. And reach out for more fresh vegetables, especially the dark green leafy types.

A wider range of nutrients can be assured by taking food supplements. These special sources of vitamins and minerals have probably been consumed since the earliest days of human history, albeit in a different form than you and I know today. Evidence for the naturalness of supplements comes not just from excavations of ancient human settlements but from studies of the diets of primitive people now living who haven't yet switched to a processed food culture.

The highland dwellers of Peru, for example, burn rocks and plant stalks and make the residue into paste or powder which is very high in calcium—an important mineral in which many

Americans are deficient. Corn-eating Indians of North and South America avoid protein and niacin deficiency by adding ash or lime to their corn, thus improving the amino acid balance and making more niacin available. Bread made from corn by contemporary Hopi Indians of our Southwest was found to contain forty times more calcium, five times more magnesium, eight times more manganese, three times more iron, and seven times more zinc than regular cornmeal.

There's also plenty of evidence that primitive peoples around the world have burned certain plants to get an ash that tasted salty, which they used as a seasoning. A study of the Sanio-Hiowe people in New Guinea showed that the ash they were getting by burning the sago palm was rich in potassium. So as a "salt" it was much healthier than the usual sodium salt, which can be a cause of high blood pressure. But even more interesting, this rich potassium food supplement the Sanio-Hiowe people were making did something to their metabolism which enabled them to live healthily on smaller amounts of protein. That unique finding is reported by P. K. Townsend and colleagues in a 1973 issue of *Ecology of Food and Nutrition*.

We need such food supplements even more than our ancestors and present-day primitives. They feasted on wild or semiwild plants and animals often eaten fresh and raw, with none of their fiber, vitamins, and minerals stripped away by processing. On the other hand, most of the food we can buy in stores today is derived from plants that have been puffed up by scientific breeding into gross enlargements of the wild things people used to eat. Instead of eating tiny wild apples and rich little berries that literally burst with vitamin C, we buy big red apples and other fruits that are a poor nutritional exchange for their wild originals. People like their rather bland taste and attractive color, but an analytical look at their insides reveals that much of their vitamin value has been traded away for commercial values like appearance and storability.

Mankind grew up on a whole range of primitive foods which simply isn't available now to most consumers. Our inner historical program still signals us to hunger for those lost days of vitamin richness and food variety. To think that a modern diet of supermarket foods can produce total health, even when "balanced" according to the ideas of an academic dietitian, is wishful thinking. Because it just isn't natural.

An Easy-to-Use Food Guide

Eating as our forebears did seems simple enough. As we've seen, though, some foods that may seem wholesome have been manipulated into health threats. And other substances eaten by our ancestors may seem unnatural to those of us who know little of ancient or remote peoples.

What's needed is a clear way to organize and visualize what is already known so we can make the right decisions about what to eat. Attempts to devise a simple food guide have been made in the past, but they haven't worked well. The guides were either too vague and simplistic, too difficult to remember and use, or wrong in the sense that they actually encouraged people to eat unhealthful foods. No currently used system is up to the task of presenting a clear picture of the growing mass of information about food that's now available.

Consider the old "eat a balanced diet" admonition, for example. Perhaps that idea made some sense in the days before widespread processing of food, when there weren't so many booby-trapped foods in supermarket aisles. If you "balanced" your diet then by eating a little of everything, at least you avoided getting a deficiency disease. But what does that word *balanced* really mean? Should food be balanced by weight, by vitamin value, by protein content, or what?

It is confusing, to say the least.

The current fashion among nutritionists is to place all food into one of four groups and to encourage meal selection from those groups. The first category is milk and dairy products. The second is fruits and vegetables. Group three includes eggs, dry beans, peas, and nuts, as well as meat, poultry, and fish. The fourth group is breads and cereals.

That system is confusing, too. Who among us thinks about food groups when ordering in a restaurant or selecting food in a market? We have enough trouble worrying about how to pay for food, without feeling obliged to check its category in some arbitrary group.

Also, the food-group system doesn't do enough to warn people about bad foods or foods which have bad qualities, such as excessive fat or salt. Other foods are simply dumb concoctions of processed ingredients with chemical additives, and people need some way to keep reminding themselves not to eat them. The food-group system doesn't measure up to that need. The best diet plan should focus your attention on the foods you know are excellent, and must remind you to avoid those foods which are harmful or lack solid value.

Most important of all, a food guide should encourage you to eat more of the good foods. That's perfectly obvious, but surprisingly, the older food guides don't do that. The balanced diet advice implies that eating too much of one kind of food isn't good. Guides based on food groups also say clearly that centering your diet around foods that fit into fewer than all four groups leads to trouble. There's a strong implication in those systems that variety in food choices is more important than other factors, such as a food's basic nutritional quality.

A far better approach is to focus your attention on the relatively small number of foods that you know are excellent in all respects. In developing that personal list of foods, consider all factors that contribute to quality. That would include not only whether the food contains plentiful vitamins and minerals, but also whether it is free of contamination, rich in badly needed complex carbohydrates, high in fiber, low in fat, reasonable in cost, and easy to prepare if your time is limited. And of course, you should enjoy its flavor.

Get in the habit of thinking of all foods as occupying a place on a sliding scale of quality. Then, when shopping, planning meals, or choosing from a restaurant menu, always lean toward those better foods.

I'll go even further and suggest that you make a habit of eating certain extra-good foods over and over again—day after day. That's getting pretty far from the wide variety of choice inherent in the balanced diet concept, but actually (in a way) it's what most people are now doing. The problem is that they tend to eat fatty meats and relatively bad foods containing white flour and sugar at almost every meal. Habits like that seldom disappear on their own. They must be replaced by other habits. To move yourself away from bad food ideas, fix your mind on a certain number of good foods and eat them regularly.

Eating the same food over and over is far from being a new idea in human nutrition. Many reports of the eating habits of ancient peoples who enjoyed good health show that they tended to center their diet around a few basic foods of high nutritional value. That is still done today by peoples living in cultures insulated from modern technology. For example, the Dani people of New Guinea live happily and healthfully on a diet that is 90 percent sweet potatoes, of which they grow 70 different varieties. And Eskimos living in their traditional culture thrive on a diet consisting mostly of fatty meat and raw fish, with an occasional wild bird for variety. Such peoples have always kept an eye peeled for special herbs, greens, nuts, berries, seeds, and so forth that they knew from experience made them feel good, but the core of their diet was often a limited food selection. And it served them well, for they seldom developed the cancer, heart disease, diabetes, arthritis, and other chronic diseases of civilization that afflict Americans.

Foods available to us now that will support the highest level of health can be remembered most easily if they are arranged in the form of a pictorial diagram. A target seems especially appropriate, for it gives us a place for the great foods in the bull's-eye, and also lets us show beyond the last scoring ring those foods which miss the mark completely. Between the great and the bad we can position all the other foods on a sliding scale of value.

The target diagram that is reproduced here was prepared with a good deal of thought. But it needn't be exactly the one you use, because everyone is somewhat different and has different taste preferences, or even food allergies. (Wheat, for example, can be OK for most people but terribly bad for those with a wheat allergy.) Granted there are in the bull's-eye foods that some people may not care for. But we get to like what we eat regularly. While flavor is extremely important, even more important is the need to think about the great benefits you'll receive from eating foods which are solidly good for you as well as flavorful. In other words, give yourself a chance to learn to like better foods, instead of letting fatty, sugary, salted, and manipulated foods take over your taste buds. After a short period of getting used to the more subtle flavors of a natural food diet, you won't miss the rich, doctored-up foods at all.

Here are some of the reasons why foods are placed where they are on our target diagram. First, the bull's-eye.

Fish is closest to the center. A major reason for giving it that honor is the fact that fish is a staple food in many of the healthiest ancient and modern societies. In doing background research for this target plan, we found fish in closer association with the diet of healthy people than any other food. It's low in saturated fat, rich in protein, vitamins, and minerals, and often of excellent flavor. The only problem with fish is that it tends to be expensive. Also keep in mind that the lighter textured fish like haddock and flounder are lower in fat (and therefore in calories) than are other types.

Rice is another food like fish—successfully eaten by millions of healthy people. Rice is also good-tasting and cheap. The brown kind (richer in fiber, vitamins, and minerals) is in the bull's-eye. That great fiber food, bran, is near the center of the chart, and so is wheat germ, an excellent B-vitamin source. (Both should be eaten in moderation, though, because they are supplementary foods.) Corn is near the middle, and so are sunflower seeds. Bean sprouts are right there, too—even closer to the middle than beans themselves because sprouts have added nutritional value. Oats are another grain in the bull's-eye, because of their high protein, good fiber, and a flavor that can make day-after-day eating enjoyable.

I've put sweet potatoes in the middle, too, because they're

so rich in good food elements like vitamin A and are another healthful food you can enjoy eating regularly. White potatoes are only slightly less healthful—but still are excellent if prepared simply (not eaten as potato chips). Garlic is in the bull's-eye for its antibiotic nature and its beneficial effects on the circulatory system.

Dark green leafy vegetables are in the center because they're so necessary to many people as a source of calcium and vitamin A. Fruits are great foods, as we all know, but they're slightly away from the middle because of an often high sugar content.

Keep in mind also that fruits vary in quality, depending on how long and under what conditions they've been stored. An apple picked and eaten fresh from a tree in your yard usually has more vitamin value than a soft, mealy apple that's been kept on a store shelf for weeks or even months. Some varieties of fruits are also richer in nutrients than others.

All meats are out of the bull's-eye, to varying degrees. That doesn't mean we think meat is bad, by any means. But since the American diet is already so overloaded with fat from overuse of lard, oils, butter, and other dairy products, we're almost forced to place most meat visually where you won't think of it as a key to a more healthful diet. Chicken—served without its skin—is the best. Turkey has the same value for our diagraming purposes.

Some foods are completely out of the scoring area of the target. Most are what I call foods of civilization, which simply weren't available to us in any quantity during the period of our genetic development. We can't handle such foods in more than trace quantities without causing a malfunction in one or more of our basic metabolic systems. Most of these "outside-the-ring" foods can't ever balance a diet—only cause a harmful imbalance.

Most likely all of us will keep eating some of these off-target foods. But it is important to know that in the purest sense of a good diet, they are out-of-bounds.

If you are puzzled by the arbitrariness of this target system of food choice planning, keep in mind two things.

First, the target ratings I have given to different foods represent my judgment of what foods are of most and least value. (I have, however, used some of the food-rating suggestions of

Nutrition Action, in particular those given in "Updating the Basic Four," an article published in the January 1979 issue.) You can, and perhaps should, make your own personalized food-target diagram. Adjust it to suit your own tastes and the time of the year when certain good foods may be in season and others aren't available. Use your knowledge about food quality, plus what you learn by further study, to further personalize your chart.

Also remember that the main function of this target system is to encourage you to change your thinking about the quantities of different foods that you eat, as well as their quality. The idea of a balanced diet avoids that question of differing quantities of foods entirely, which is wrong. I think people should be willing to eat more of the good foods and less of the questionable, and the vision of a good diet that you have in your head should encourage strongly that way of thinking.

In my experience, you can always ask a truly healthy person, "What foods sustain you?" and get a clear answer. Most often such people will mention a very few basic foods of excellent quality. Perhaps without thinking about it they have worked out a system much like this food-target diagram, and are putting it to good use.

An Anticancer Program

ancer is such an important health problem that we simply can't afford to wait until it has been diagnosed before beginning to think about it, or before taking action against it. Even prevention in the usual sense is not enough. The accepted steps in cancer prevention focus primarily on avoiding the carcinogens. That includes not smoking, trying to live in an unpolluted place, and avoiding potentially dangerous food additives. Do those things and your chances of developing cancer should be reduced. But there are many people who have not done them, yet who want as much as anyone else to avoid cancer. And remember, it is the nature of cancer to begin twenty or more years after exposure to a carcinogen.

Who among us can say with certainty that he or she hasn't eaten, touched, or breathed a carcinogen sometime in the past? I can remember playing with pieces of asbestos, a potent carcinogen, several times during my youth. Probably everyone has had similar contacts, because we live in a technological society that is literally awash with carcinogens.

What is needed is a system of cancer suppression that can become an easy, regular, inexpensive, and enjoyable part of our lives. We have to assume that somewhere, at some time, we have been exposed to a carcinogen, or perhaps a whole series of carcinogens. Now we must not only prevent further contact with carcinogens, but must protect ourselves from the cancer promoters as well. We even need to eat regularly things that will counter the growth of cancer itself. For maximum health, we should act throughout our lives as if cancerous cells have started growing somewhere in our bodies.

I believe that the suppression of those malignant cells is now possible. Within the past few years enough hard information about dietary and other means to head off cancer has been published in scientific journals to bring the dream of protection against this disease much closer to being a reality. I have examined all these findings carefully and have seen that they can be put together into a program for action that is practical, safe, and easy to follow. Yes, some changes in the way you eat and live will be necessary. Yes, you are going to have to keep some simple facts about health and food in mind. But this program is simple and inexpensive, and will yield benefits that you may be able to see and feel immediately. Just the saving in money alone could make the whole idea very worthwhile—with the hope of preventing cancer thrown in as a wonderful bonus.

Here are the elements of this cancer-suppression system:

Avoid smoking and smokers. So much has been said about smoking and cancer that I hardly feel it is necessary to say more. However, remember that smoking can increase the harm done by other carcinogens, such as asbestos. You should also be aware of findings that show nonsmokers exposed to tobacco smoke for the equivalent of a workday suffer lung damage similar to smokers puffing up to half a pack a day. Moreover, benzopyrene, which is one of the most potent carcinogens in tobacco, is released in particle form in cigarette smoke.

Eat less fat and red meat. This could be the most important part of your cancer-suppression program. The digestion of fats is helped by bile acid excreted by the liver. Many cancer researchers feel that bile acid is a major factor in the cause of cancer of the colon. If you eat less fat, your lower intestinal tract will be subject to much smaller quantities of that cancer promoter.

Americans eat far too much fat anyway. Look around and you'll see that about four out of every ten people are overweight. I believe our massive overweight problem is caused more by the use of too much butter, oil, margarine, and fatty meat than by any other dietary factor. Some studies indicate that being overweight and eating too much are associated with cancer.

There is also much evidence that beef is a cancer promoter. The case against beef is not airtight, but it is impressive. Followers of the Seventh-Day Adventist religion, who tend to be vegetarians, get less cancer than others. Non-beef eaters in general tend to be resistant.

Reducing your beef and other meat consumption could very well save you plenty of money. True, many people love the taste of beef and, as I said in an earlier chapter, meat is an important source of many nutrients. But the more you know about the harm it can do to your health, the worse it begins to taste. Think of all the harmful chemicals that are in meat, especially beef. The General Accounting Office reported in 1979 that 143 drugs and pesticides used in connection with livestock production are likely to leave residues in raw meat and poultry. Of those, no less than 42 are known to cause, or are suspected of causing, cancer. Twenty cause birth defects and 6 cause mutations.

Carol Tucker Foreman, former assistant secretary of agriculture for food and consumer services of the U.S. Department of Agriculture, has warned that that agency is monitoring the presence of only 46 of those 143 harmful drugs and pesticides that can be in meat. That's because the USDA has testing methods for only 46 of those compounds.

You should especially avoid eating bacon, because it contains no less than four factors which can increase cancer risk. First, it is very fatty. Second, it contains nitrites. Third, the high heat at which bacon is cooked increases nitrosamine production. And fourth, bacon is salty, and a high-salt intake will accelerate nitrosamine production.

Get plenty of dietary fiber. Bran and other fibrous foods create greater intestinal bulk and also dilute the intestinal contents by soaking up more fluids. That reduces the contact of possible cancer promoters with the walls of the intestines. Also, the speed of passage of food material through the intestines is increased, and possibly this may reduce the time that any cancer promoters are against intestinal walls. Although it has not yet been proven beyond doubt that those effects are vital to cancer prevention, the use of dietary fiber confers other benefits and can hardly cause harm.

Consume adequate amounts of vitamins and minerals. Vitamins function by working with enzymes which are extremely important to the body's self-purification efforts. Research into the role of vitamins in suppressing cancer has just begun, yet already there is a flow of reports into the literature that they can have a significant effect. So far, vitamin A has received the most attention, with promising results reported by several different researchers. I believe we will soon see much wider use of vitamin A as a cancer preventer.

Vitamin C is also now considered to have value as an anticancer factor. Linus Pauling and other researchers are convinced that it can prevent or even cure cancer, and several books now document that ten grams a day or more of vitamin C has greatly eased the pain of numerous cancer patients and also significantly prolonged the lives of some of them.

"We can conclude that vitamin E may help prevent cancer of the breast," Robert London, M.D., said not long ago. He is director of obstetrical and gynecological research at Mount Sinai Hospital in Baltimore. Vitamin B_6 was called "an acceptable form of secondary cancer prevention" in an article in the journal *Nutrition and Cancer*. Evidence indicates it can reduce the incidence of recurring bladder tumors.

Among the minerals, selenium is of major interest as a cancer preventer. Gerhard N. Schrauzer, Ph.D., has analyzed data from seventeen countries and found that there is less breast cancer wherever people have more selenium in their blood. And new evidence is emerging that when cancer patients on chemotherapy are given supplements of vitamins A and C as well as of selenium, the effectiveness of their therapy is greatly increased—even in types of cancer usually resistant to chemotherapy. The trace elements magnesium and zinc have also been associated with cancer prevention. If you aren't already taking supplements, you should be.

Eat generously of anticancer foods. The rapidly increasing pace of nutrition research is opening our eyes to the power that certain foods have to inhibit the action of carcinogens or the growth of cancer. Some of these reported effects could be the result of the vitamins in foods. That's the opinion of John H. Weisburger, Ph.D., a researcher with the American Health Foundation. He wrote in *Nutrition and Cancer* that the decrease in stomach cancer in the United States over the last fifty years could be the result of increased regular eating of foods containing vitamin C.

It also looks as though some foods have a cancer-suppressing power that goes beyond the effect of their vitamin content. "There is increasing evidence that diet is a major environmental modifier of the carcinogenesis process." That sentence, written by researchers at the University of Texas System Cancer Center in Houston, began an article in *Nutrition and Cancer* that reported that there is an anticancer effect in sprouts of wheat, mung beans, and lentils. Health food advocates had been saying for years that sprouts were healthful for many nutritional reasons, but only the lone voice of Ann Wigmore, Ph.D., had claimed intuitively that wheat sprouts suppressed cancer. For years I thought she was making too strong a claim, but now I'm wondering whether it's possible to say too many good things about sprouts. More recently, Drs. Lai, Dabney, and Shaw, who did the sprout research in Houston, have indicated that chlorophyll could be the active substance in sprouts that makes them effective against cancer.

Broccoli, cabbage, and brussels sprouts also may combat malignancies. Folklore has long attributed health values to these related vegetables, which are all members of the Brassica group of species. In 1978, however, a team of researchers directed by Saxon Graham, Ph.D., talked to many people with colon or rectal cancer and found that they ate less of these vegetables than did people not suffering from those diseases. They even reported a specific effect of cabbage against cancer of the rectum, while sauerkraut, coleslaw, brussels sprouts, and broccoli were more effective against cancer of the colon. Studies with rats confirmed the human observations. The results were reported in the *Journal of the National Cancer Institute.*

Seeds may turn out to be even more valuable as cancer preventers than are vegetables. And I believe that the soybean could have the most potential as a healthful supplement to our normal diet.

Soycrafting for Better Health

If we are going to eat less meat to improve our health, we need an alternative food, and soybeans are an excellent choice. The fact that those Japanese people who eat the most soybeans tend to get less cancer than others is especially encouraging. Epidemiological evidence of that type is the catalyst which has caused Walter Troll, Ph.D., a research professor in the department of environmental medicine at New York University to investigate the diet-cancer link in a new way.

Dr. Troll had thought about the fact that people who are vegetarians or who tend toward vegetarianism have less cancer.

He had also noted that a class of substances called synthetic protease inhibitors countered the effect of chemicals which can cause skin cancer. Dr. Troll then got the idea of feeding soybeans—which contain natural protease inhibitors—to test animals that were made susceptible to cancer by x-ray treatments or applications of cancer-causing chemicals. Working with Drs. Sidney Belman, Rakoma Wiesner, and Claire J. Shellabarger, he carried out those tests.

In two different test situations the soybean diets worked. Rats fed soybeans were protected against breast cancer, and mice against skin cancer. The evidence for a similar effect in humans is highly suggestive. In a published abstract describing his work, Dr. Troll commented that "Natural-occurring protease inhibitors such as those found in soybeans may offer a novel method of preventing cancer in man."

What is it about protease inhibitors which causes them to have an anticancer effect? No one knows. Dr. Troll would like to be able to explain what is happening in metabolic terms, but as yet there isn't enough clear information available to do that. If soybeans were a drug in the normal sense, their unknown mode of action against a disease would be ample reason to wait until more research was in before recommending them for use. But soybeans aren't a medication. They are a food, which happens to contain substances that have been found to have an effect against one of the most life-threatening of all diseases. So we should not hesitate to use them enthusiastically.

While we are uncertain how the protease inhibitors do their anticancer work, they are extremely fascinating substances, with many functions in nature. One of their main jobs is to guard the protein in seeds. Soybeans, which have more protein than other seeds and beans, are rich in protease inhibitors.

Many health-minded people are aware that these substances limit the extent to which certain amino acids—the building blocks of protein—can be used by the body. It is also widely known that the activity of the inhibitors is reduced when the soybeans are cooked, allowing better protein utilization. Some people are afraid of certain soybean products, like flour, thinking that perhaps it isn't cooked enough and will hurt them.

There is a certain amount of confusion on this issue among the experts, but the general feeling is that concern about cooking soybeans and soybean products is overdone. Actually, the inhibitors are reduced to levels that allow more efficient utilization of protein after only a short cooking time. But if soybean foods are processed at very high heat over long periods of time, then the content of inhibitors will be cut to the point where there is no apparent anticancer effect. So you may want to look for ways to use them that require only moderate cooking.

Dr. Troll feels that sprouted and roasted soybeans are sources having a valuable inhibitor content. Soybeans can also be prepared in a wide variety of other ways, most of which provide good levels of protease inhibitors.

The news that soybeans may be useful for cancer prevention comes at an exciting time for this important legume food—a gift to us from the Orient. Production of soybeans by farmers is booming. It is now the most important cash crop of American farms. There is a reason for that. Soybeans provide a home on their roots for a type of bacteria which is extremely efficient at taking nitrogen from the air and putting it to use for the growth of the soybean plant. That allows the soybean to grow abundantly with less cost for fertilizer than other plants.

Beans are already looked on by most cooks as cheap foods, and soybeans are super cheap. Perhaps their cheapness, combined with their uniquely high nutritional value, is one reason soybeans haven't fit more directly into typical menu plans. They are a food by themselves, in a manner of speaking, and call for special attention.

That situation is changing rapidly, though. People are waking up to the many ways that soybeans can be used, and they especially enjoy the fact that soybeans can provide excellent nutrition without costing an arm and a leg. Roasted soybeans, for example, are very popular as a snack food and have the special advantage of being a snack with fine nutritional value. With the new knowledge that roasted soybeans can also be used as part of a cancer-prevention diet, their popularity is bound to increase still further.

Defatted soy flour and soy grits are also good bets nutritionally. They can easily be used as supplements to wheat flour in baking, to improve the protein content of foods as well as to get some of the other benefits of eating soybeans. Another option is to buy plain, whole soybeans in a health food store and prepare them as you would regular beans. They need soaking first, of course, and require more cooking time than other beans because they're so dense and packed with oil as well as protein. But many natural foods cooks use whole soybeans regularly, with excellent results.

Sprouting is a useful way to improve both the nutritional value and the flavor of soybeans. They are somewhat more difficult to sprout than mung beans, which are the more commonly used for that purpose, and seem to need more frequent watering and a cooler temperature during sprouting. One way to simplify the process is to do what I think of as half-sprouting. Soak the beans overnight, then rinse them for a day or two—until the stems peep out of the beans. Then cook these partially sprouted soybeans as you would regular beans. The cooking time should be much reduced, and perhaps more of the valuable protease inhibitors will be saved, which is an important advantage.

If you're willing to think beyond the scope of quick meal preparation, you can easily see a large spectrum of other soybean food possibilities. Soycrafting is the name that's been given to this adventure, which is as much a gift to us from the Orient as is the soybean itself. I advise you to think of soycrafting as having three major benefits: (1) you can use it to produce a whole range of good-tasting foods for your family at exceptionally low cost; (2) you can do more to prevent or control cancer by increasing dramatically the amount of soy foods you eat; (3) if you're looking for a small business to go into—small enough to be operated from your home, if necessary—you'll find opportunity in soycrafting.

The soybean has often been called "the cow of China," and for good reason. The oil, protein, and some of the minerals that are in regular milk are packaged neatly inside each soybean. All that's missing is water, and some heat to emulsify the mixture.

Soybeans are hydrophilic, which means they accept water readily. Soak them in water overnight, and each pound of beans will become about 2½ pounds. When warmed up and squeezed, they will give milk. Of course, grinding is necessary to break up the beans. But the whole process is quite simple and can easily be done at home. The final step in making the milk is squeezing the ground and cooked beans through several layers of cheese-cloth.

You can drink soy milk if you want, or use it in all the different ways people normally use milk. Up to now, the big market for it has been among people allergic to cows' milk. Many infants have that allergy, and some adults have it and don't know it. Cows' milk, in my opinion, is not a good food for adults, not only for allergy reasons but because it is high in saturated fat and contains cholesterol. Using soy milk avoids those problems.

Soy milk is the basic product from which many soycrafted foods are made. Just as cows' milk can be made into cheese, ice cream, yogurt, and other things, soy milk can be made into bean curd (tofu), soy milk ice cream, and soy yogurt. Tofu is a much better food than cheese because it's not salty, is not as fatty, and has protease inhibitors. The Chinese call tofu "meat without bones," which is a good description. Americans still have much to learn about how to use tofu in cooking, but this Oriental staple is now being sold fresh or canned in larger supermarkets here, and the day when it will seriously compete with meat may not be far away.

Here is a quick description of how tofu is made. A coagu-lating agent—such as calcium sulfate or magnesium chloride (*nigari*)—is mixed into hot soy milk. The mixture is stirred, causing the milk to coagulate into curds, and whey (the remaining fluid part of the milk) appears. The whey is strained off and the curds are ladled into a tofu-forming box where pressure is applied so that more whey comes out. After ten to fifteen minutes of pressure, the pressed curds are taken out, and there you have it—tofu! The whole process of making tofu from soy milk takes about an hour.

The economics of soycrafting, if examined closely, reveal why interest in soybean processing is increasing so rapidly. Or-ganically grown soybeans, which most soycrafters use, cost about twenty-six dollars per hundred pounds when bought in large quantities. After soybeans are soaked in water, though, their weight increases dramatically. A good tofu maker can turn out 2½ to 3 pounds of product per pound of beans, and that tofu can sell at retail for one dollar a pound or more. Commercial soycrafting shops give people a way to offer a real service to their customers and make a profit at the same time.

Tofu can be made at home for as little as ten or fifteen cents a pound, if you don't consider your own time as part of the cost. In addition to being cheaper, homemade tofu tastes better than the commercial kind. When made commercially, tofu is cooled in flowing water to keep it from spoiling. That washes out much of the flavorful whey. Homemade tofu can be cooled in air, and therefore keeps in more of its flavor. (However, homemade tofu which won't be eaten soon after it is made should also be stored in water to prevent spoilage.) The Chinese cool tofu that way and are very fussy about buying it the same day it's made, when the flavor is best.

Another promising soy food from Southeast Asia is tempeh, a fermented product made from lightly cooked soybeans. It is usually fried, and is excellent in sandwiches. Although tempeh is still not as readily available as tofu, its production will probably increase because it resembles meat and fish in both taste and texture.

Imitation meats and meat-extenders are made from textured vegetable protein (TVP) which is "spun" from soybeans. My preference is for foods that don't require elaborate factory processing before they get to my plate, so I'm not a fan of TVP. But if you can get TVP foods that aren't flavored or colored artificially, you may want to give them a try.

A unique and excellent way to prepare soybeans has been developed by INTSOY, the International Soybean Program at 113 Mumford Hall, University of Illinois, Urbana 61801. INTSOY's mission is to help people in underdeveloped countries make better use of soybeans. One concern of INTSOY is the shortage of cooking fuel in many Third World countries. In response to that problem, it has developed ways for people to cook soybeans at home quickly, saving heat. We can use the INTSOY method for another purpose—to keep more of the protease inhibitors in our soybean foods.

If you try this approach, don't soak the beans. Crack them

by running them through a hand flour mill set so that each bean is broken into about twenty pieces. (Burr plate mills, such as the Corona, sold by mail or in health food stores, work well.) Put about four ounces of crushed beans in about three cups of boiling water. Simmer for ten minutes. Add about eleven ounces of raw, peeled, and diced sweet potatoes and cook for fifteen minutes more, stirring occasionally. Then, pass the cooked mixture through the grinder again, but this time set it at high tension, for fine grinding. The mixture can then be reheated and served as a breakfast food. Or, if made with less water, it can be formed into patties and fried.

We've made and eaten this INTSOY dish, as well as variations using corn and whole wheat with soybeans. I prefer the soy-sweet potato mixture, because sweet potatoes are very rich in vitamin A, which also has anticancer properties. Soy-sweet potato patties could be an ideal cancer-preventing food. All variations of the recipe taste excellent, though. The cost is low, and it is healthful and nourishing. INTSOY suggests adding a small amount of bicarbonate of soda to the cooking water to speed cooking time. That could reduce the amount of protease inhibitor in the food, so we didn't do it.

Other interesting foods can be made with what Japanese call *okara*, and American soy milk makers *soy fines*. It is the fiber-rich pulp left after the milk is squeezed from cooked beans. Okara can be added to baked goods or casseroles, or made into soysage, which is a popular meatless form of sausage. The outer hulls of soybeans are now also being sold in tablet form as soy bran. It does the same things for your health as wheat bran.

There are plenty of ways soybeans can be used to improve our diet, save money, and supply us with the protease inhibitors that we need. But at least I've suggested a few of the many possibilities open to you. With our new understanding that protease inhibitors could be of great importance to our health—and not something to be feared—we can bring the soybean out of its anonymous role in processed foods and into the mainstream of delicious foods that safeguard health.

Special Diets Worth Trying

Almost every physical and mental quality—from strength and endurance to mental tranquility and the ability to resist disease—can in some way be influenced by the kinds of food you eat.

How do you find out what to eat to achieve a desired effect on your body? The answer is—experiment! Try different diet systems and note the effect that they have on you. Many people do that naturally, without thinking that such experimenting is any big deal. "I never eat onions because they give me gas," you have probably heard someone say. Onions were identified as the culprit by a very personal but effective research process; namely, trial and error. Yet the relief that comes from the simple discovery that onions produce indigestion far exceeds the benefits that that person could get from research which is not so personal. The greatest medical miracles sometimes occur in our own heads.

Can the frontiers of personal diet experimentation be expanded? I think they can. In fact, we are seeing now a proliferation of unusual diet suggestions that are aimed at preventing or "controlling" chronic, degenerative diseases, the cures for which have eluded laboratory researchers. Some of these diet ideas are extremely odd and require a considerable degree of diligence. Yet the promise of cure that they offer—if trials show them to be truly effective—is indeed remarkable. One such diet involves avoiding tomatoes and their relatives.

As almost everyone knows, the tomato was once considered to be poisonous. Then a few brave souls started eating those attractive red fruits and the secret was out. "Tomatoes taste good, and they don't hurt you!" Today, the tomato is perhaps the most important vegetable in dozens of countries. But that hasn't stopped Norman F. Childers, Ph.D., professor of horticulture at Rutgers University in New Jersey, from questioning the healthfulness of tomatoes and certain other related plants. He has written and published a book called *The Nightshades and Health* (©1977 by Norman F. Childers, printed by Somerset Press, Somerville, N.J.), which presents circumstantial evidence linking the eating of tomatoes, white potatoes, peppers, and eggplant—and the use of tobacco as well—with arthritis and rheumatism.

Are you surprised to hear that the tomato, white potato, pepper, and eggplant are members of the nightshade family? As Dr. Childers points out, other members of that clan of plants have been labeled as toxic for a long time. The black and the deadly nightshade are famous poisonous plants, and drugs such as belladonna, atropine, and scopolamine are made from nightshade derivatives. So when you think about it, the tomato, white potato, pepper, and eggplant do come from a family with more than a few skeletons in its closet.

Dr. Childers doesn't say that these common food plants are toxic to everyone. His theory is that only 5 to 10 percent of the population is susceptible to some toxic element they contain. What happens when susceptible people eat those plants? Dr. Childers claims that they get arthritis and rheumatism, and that there is a remote possibility that some other health problems can also result. That's indeed a fascinating idea, if true. No one has yet found the cause of arthritis and rheumatism, and no field of medical science has led to more dead ends than arthritis research, with the possible exception of attempts to cure cancer. Could it be that a horticultural scientist has finally tripped on a clue to the arthritis-rheumatism problem that will lead to relief for at least some of the 31.6 million Americans now being treated for this complex disease?

While Dr. Childers is a respected scientist and teacher, he is not presenting the nightshade-arthritis theory as an outgrowth of his mainstream scientific work. He is primarily an expert in fruit culture, and has written one of the most widely used texts on promology, the science of fruit growing.

The nightshade-arthritis theory came to him as a flash of inspiration, after observing what foods made his own joint and muscle pain better or worse. More or less by accident, he stopped eating tomatoes for a period of time and noticed improvement in a stiff neck condition. For a long time, he kept that observation to himself, thinking it wasn't anything important. But then a secretary in his office who was suffering from a bad case of arthritis gave the idea a push forward. Dr. Childers suggested she stay away from white potatoes as well as other nightshade foods, and her arthritis is now completely gone. That lady told others, who tried the idea and found that it worked. Dr. Childers also located over eight hundred arthritis-rheumatism sufferers with the help of a few small newspaper advertisements, word of mouth, and mentions at meetings, and found that most had some degree of relief when they followed the no-nightshade diet.

"It's a very difficult diet to follow," Dr. Childers concedes. "You find tomatoes, white potatoes, and peppers in a wide variety of dishes, and they must all be avoided to give the diet a chance to work. Even paprika on fish can cause a reaction in sensitive people," he claims. His book contains long lists of prepared foods that contain nightshades. They range from clam chowder to prepared salad dressings and even hot dogs. Seasonings containing paprika and other red peppers are used widely in processed foods. Dr. Childers also lists many foods that are substitutes for white potatoes, tomatoes, peppers, and eggplant.

According to Dr. Childers and his co-author, Gerard M. Russo, younger people in the early stages of arthritis pain benefit most from the diet. If there is bone, joint, or tendon damage as a result of long-term affliction, improvement comes more slowly.

For some people, apparently, the results can be dramatic. When *Prevention* readers were invited to take part in an informal study of the no-nightshade diet, nearly half of the 290 people who returned the final questionnaire described a better than 50 percent improvement in their symptoms. And 44 participants—15 percent of the sample—reported their arthritis more than 85 percent improved, describing major reductions in joint tenderness, pain, and muscle spasm, as well as big gains in range of motion and in exercise endurance. Many of these people were able to cut back on potentially hazardous arthritis medications. And some volunteered that their physical improvement had given them a brighter outlook on life.

If arthritis and rheumatism are not your problem, but you're worried about diabetes or hypertension, you might want to give some thought to a diet of raw foods. That's the suggestion of John M. Douglass, M.D., and Irving M. Rasgon, M.D., physicians in the department of internal medicine and family practice of the Southern California Permanente Medical Group in Los Angeles.

Why avoid hot meals? Drs. Douglass and Rasgon use the persuasive rationale that early man lived entirely on raw foods and the structure and functioning of our digestive system hasn't changed much, if at all, in over one hundred thousand years.

Modern-day foods that can be eaten raw are great in number. Dr. Douglass suggests vegetables, seeds, nuts, berries, melons, other fruits, egg yolks, honey, oils, and goat's milk. Raw goat's milk is recommended because, as Dr. Douglass says, "there is much less risk of brucellosis or tuberculosis from it than from raw cow's milk." He advises avoiding raw meat and fish because of parasite infestation problems.

Eating only raw foods is an extreme diet idea that has been used by some health enthusiasts for many years. The two reasons for a raw diet that I've heard most often are that heating food lowers vitamin content and that it destroys certain enzymes. People who enjoy a cup of hot soup and cooked meat and vegetables have countered by saying they can still get plenty of vitamins from other sources. And doctors point out that the body manufactures its own enzymes and destroys through digestion those present in food.

Drs. Douglass and Rasgon take another tack. First, they have seen with their own eyes that some diabetics who eat predominately raw foods can often get along without insulin. Their reports of these observations have appeared in *Lancet* and *Annals of Internal Medicine*—both highly respected journals. One of the most dramatic cases was that of a severe juvenile diabetic who was able to stop using insulin and eventually oral antidiabetic drugs by following a 90 to 100 percent raw food diet.

There have been other successes, but not all diabetics observed were able to plan a raw food diet that kept carbohydrate levels manageable. One man who failed with the diet, despite eating 80 percent raw foods, was found to be consuming eighteen bananas each day. That was simply too much carbohydrate from a fruit source.

The two physicians believe that the raw food diet helps diabetics by moving food very rapidly through the digestive system. A normal diet of cooked and processed foods passes through the gut in eighty to one hundred hours. A high raw-foods diet goes through in only eighteen to twenty-four hours. While food is languishing in the intestines, say the physicians, it may be throwing off chemicals that "poison some of the systems involved in carbohydrate metabolism and aggravate a diabetic condition." The absorption of carbohydrate from raw foods is also a much smoother process, they say.

Again, we are dealing with a diet that isn't easy to follow. If you eat only raw foods you have to avoid most restaurants, buy foods differently, and make special demands on your family and friends. Not to mention giving up many dishes that you enjoy eating.

The benefits of a raw food diet could be worth all that trouble, though. Not only would a diabetic likely be able to reduce or avoid drugs, but blood pressure would be lowered, too. Dr. Douglass reports "promising" experimental results with a group of thirty-two hypertensives who recently tried a 60 to 100 percent raw food diet. Their blood pressure was lowered significantly.

An extra benefit of the diet could be a solid break with some of the bad habits of Western living. Subjects in the hypertension test reported that if they cut out cooked foods almost entirely for a month or more, they no longer felt good about drinking alcohol or smoking cigarettes. One person got severe hyperventilation after taking a drink, and some others complained of nausea after smoking.

It seems that a return to our prehistoric raw food diet does for the innards what a trip to Colonial Williamsburg does for the head. Within weeks, we are transported internally back to an earlier time, literally before the invention of alcohol and cigarettes. Those health-wreckers are then easily avoided.

There's also good evidence that a diet of raw foods can prevent cancer. That effect was reported in 1972 by Saxon Graham, Ph.D., and his colleagues at the State University of New York at Buffalo. He matched cancer patients at the Roswell Park Memorial Hospital with people of similar age, ethnic background, and economic status who didn't have cancer. The non-cancer people were found to habitually eat more uncooked vegetables than the cancer victims.

Why do cooked-food eaters get more cancer? Dr. Graham thinks it's because vitamins have been cooked out of their food, or because raw vegetables have more fiber.

(Fiber in food—such as bran and the cellulose and pectin in carrots, apples, and other unrefined foods—is now believed to be an extremely important key to the prevention of some of the most important degenerative diseases, including cancer of the colon. Scientists are now developing methods for isolating and differentiating kinds of fiber. And reports are coming in that uncooked fiber, particularly that from fruits and vegetables, is the most beneficial kind.)

Plainly, these unconventional diets have a wide variety of potential benefits. The best result of all, though, could be that they teach people to take control of their own nutritional destiny. You don't have to go along with the crowd and eat all that polite, ordinary food that makes you fat, sluggish, and old before your time. You can strike off on your own and experiment with ways of eating that just might help you feel good again.

I have some suggestions about how to start your own search for a different way of eating. First, remember that as long as you get enough of the basic nutrients, a different way of eating is safe. Free yourself from the idea that you have to eat what everyone else eats. Put yourself in an adventurous frame of mind.

Second, start slowly. Once you decide on a diet, try it for one meal or a few meals. Then take a break and do more reading, studying, or investigating of your diet plan. Feed your head with information and motivation, as well as filling your stomach.

Third, remember that you're not alone. In fact, you are in good company. While vegetarians or raw-food eaters were considered the oddest of the odd only a few years ago, today eating that way is often considered fashionable. Who knows, even the no-nightshade diet could become an "in" thing one of these days.

Finally, keep alert for the feeling of inner change. Remember that by experimenting with your own customized diet you are crafting something special for your own system. Just as a made-to-measure suit of clothes fits you better on the outside, your own use-tested diet can help you be more in tune with life inside. That feeling of healthy adjustment to life is so good that it's worth the extra effort.

Wild Ways to Feel Better

Feeling good is a matter of great importance to you and me, but is not something that gets much attention from the big people in our society who like to think they're working on important problems. Giant hospitals and research centers are created to try to solve the mysteries of cancer and heart disease, and massive fund-raising campaigns are held for research into a variety of fearful ailments. But who gives much thought to helping us find ways to wake up in the morning feeling vitally alive and ready to skip through our day with a spring in our step? Hardly anybody, that's who. About the only thing we are offered from the supposedly smart folks are pills like Valium, which deaden people so they don't know whether they're feeling bad or good.

The lack of interest in feeling good as a health challenge doesn't mean the problem is not serious. It is! Tens of millions of people go through life sinking deeper and deeper into a quicksand of weakness, mental fog, and even depression. Listen to the people around you and hear what they're saying about the pace of their life. They can't sleep. They can't wake up. They feel weighted down by vague worries. In this fantastically prosperous country, they fret about not having enough material things. And the process of worrying, of course, makes feeling good even harder to achieve.

One way of raising our spirits is to get involved with the life of the earth. That can be done by starting a garden patch, no matter how small, for a garden is by definition a place of good feeling, both for plants and for people. In a garden we arrange and grow domesticated plants in ways that will allow them to thrive. By doing that we make the plants feel good, and improve our own feelings at the same time. Anyone who has ever gardened can't help but have at least a flash of good feeling every time he or she spends a few moments in a garden, no matter whose it is. The happiness of the plants gets through to those who share the space they occupy. In that purely environmental way, gardens are therapeutic.

Nutritionally, as well, gardens promote good feeling. I am convinced that much of the dragged-out, sluggish, and plain bad feeling that abounds these days is the result of not eating good food. If people could eat fresh, low-fat, vitamin-rich food from home gardens all year long they would have more energy and enthusiasm. Gardened foods, especially when grown organically, lift the spirits. They have no residues of those frightening pesticides, some of which have been known to cause sterility, and God knows what else. And they are rich in flavor, fiber, vitamins, and needed minerals, as well as nectar that makes packaged juices seem poor substitutes.

In searching for ways to feel better, we can also look beyond the garden to the wild fringes of our environment, and even at ourselves. Ourselves? Yes, we are not far removed from our primitive heritage. The easy life of civilization does not always rest easily on our shoulders. In a historical sense, we need the running and hard work that primitive people do regularly to tune ourselves to the best state of fitness. It is for that good feeling of physical wildness that so many people are jogging, running, and cycling these days. As they gain physical vigor they find the spirit soaring to new highs. There is a relation between this urge to recreate oneself and gardening, strange as that might seem to you at first. The person who runs is nurturing his or her own body the way a gardener takes care of a plant that needs help by making a special, fertile place for it. Exercise is cultivation of the physical being, and a feeling of goodness about life flows swiftly from it.

Wild places can be a refuge for people who don't have a garden, and they can even be a haven for those of us who are looking for greater elevation of spirits than our gardens can provide. And you don't have to climb Mount McKinley or tramp deep into the wilderness to find that wildness. It is all around us, in the form of wild plants that are useful.

A while back I saw an article in the journal *Economic Botany* that was pregnant with possibilities for those seeking the means to lift their spirits by eating better. Written by Thomas M. Zennie and C. Dwayne Ogwalla of the University of Cincinnati, it lists and describes the vitamin C and vitamin A content of seventeen wild plants that are found in great abundance in Ohio and Kentucky. These two gentlemen found that many of these wild plants (I hate to use the word weeds) were richer in the good things we need than some of the best-known conventional foods.

"On a weight basis," they said, "six had higher values for carotene (vitamin A) than spinach, which is reported to have one of the higher vitamin A levels of the widely marketed garden vegetables." Those six wild plants were garlic mustard, lambs-quarters, ox-eye daisy, ground ivy, plantain, and common blue violets.

Many of those plants are at their peak of value early in the spring, when people are most in need of a high-nutrient boost to their diets. And one of them, the ground ivy, offers its leaves to foragers all year long, at least in the climate of Ohio and Kentucky.

Of the seventeen wild plants that were tested in this study, fully ten had higher values for vitamin C than did oranges. One serving of each of them would provide more than the daily requirement of ascorbic acid for an average man or even for a woman during pregnancy. The plants rich in vitamin C were garlic mustard, onion grass, wild leeks, winter cress, shepherd's purse, redbud, lambs-quarters, Indian strawberry, sour grass, and common blue violets.

After reading that article in *Economic Botany* and pondering what it meant, I couldn't help but let my mind think back to the late Euell Gibbons and how his lively articles and books increased our awareness of the value of wild foods. He never claimed that people really need wild food, in the sense that they need a square meal. To him, wild foods were insurance for survival, as well as motivation for taking outdoor recreation.

I feel that we have an additional need for this wild bounty. It is a precious source of good feelings, which arise not just from the wealth of vitamins and minerals in these untamed plants, but from another gift they bring—a wider sense of the outdoors as a place where we can connect ourselves to the vital forces of the natural world. A diet of fast-food hamburgers doesn't give us all the nutrition we need to build inner strength, and the process of living on store-bought food doesn't elevate our spirits.

The big challenge, though, is the task of getting people to take wild food seriously. It is fun to read about picking ground ivy leaves in winter, or common blue violets in spring, but to go out and actually do that is another thing entirely. Most people are accustomed to getting their food in neat packages or on restaurant plates and would rather not take a chance on a weed. Our ancestors had no such inhibitions. They recognized wild plants for what they were—the source of some of the tastiest morsels available anywhere—and ate them with relish.

I, myself, have seen wild plants with fresher eyes since Rodale Press has become involved in experimental work with grain amaranth, that big teddy bear of a plant that's still part wild. Once you start gleaning those tasty white amaranth seeds or snipping off tender leaves from the young plant, you suddenly see the wild pigweed not as a pest but simply as a smaller amaranth, which is what it is. And when you look at the nutrient charts on both the weed and the grain-producing plant, you soon see how much more nutritious both of them are than much that is eaten by people who haven't opened their eyes to the wild ways to live and feel better.

Seeds and Sprouting

A gardener could be defined facetiously as someone who looks at a seed and sees a plant. Seeds are psychedelic drugs to people who tend to have loam under their fingernails. Gardeners don't have to eat seeds or smoke them in water pipes to see visions. All they have to do is listen to seeds rustle in their packets, or look at pictures in catalogs of what seeds will produce.

There are uncountable millions of nongardeners who look at seeds and see a square meal. The simple fact is that seeds are by far the most popular food in the world. You can go further and say that more than half of all human food is made from seeds. Rice, wheat, and corn are the most popular seed foods, but there are also places in the world where soybeans, millet, rye, barley, and other grains and beans are staple items of diet. And don't forget the sunflower seed, which is one of the most important sources of vegetable oil in world markets.

Plants tend to concentrate their best and most nutritious qualities in their seeds. The seed has to last through the unfavorable climatic conditions of winter, buffeted by wind and rain, freezing and thawing, and still live the next spring to provide not only chromosomes for the next generation but a substantial part of the new plant's nutrition as well. Seeds are packaged with protein, oils, minerals, and a fair amount of vitamins, too.

The Department of Agriculture Yearbook (1961) on seeds contains the interesting observation that people in the advanced industrial countries—particularly in Western Europe and the United States—don't eat nearly as much seed food as people in the less developed countries. While primitive people eat far more than half their food in the form of seeds, we fill up more on meat, potatoes, sugar, and dairy products. As a result, only about one-third of our diet is seed food.

It is also interesting that gardeners, who respect seeds for their almost mystical quality of creating life, don't do much harvesting of seeds. We leave that mainly to the farmers. We tend to concentrate instead on the fleshy part of plants—the roots, tubers, fruit, and leaves. That is good, because those parts of plants concentrate many virtues. They not only have liberal amounts of vitamins, but minerals, oils, and the best quality of carbohydrates. They taste good, too.

In recent years, though, Americans have started to discover that seeds too can be enjoyed as a fresh, growing, green vegetable. I'm talking, of course, about sprouts. Bean sprouts are an important item of food in many parts of the world, particularly in the Orient. They are also becoming more popular here every year, as we develop a taste for Oriental foods. You can find canned bean sprouts in any supermarket and fresh bean and alfalfa sprouts sometimes, too.

We should make much more use of sprouts than we do now, though, because they are a most delightful way to increase the amount of seeds we eat and add new taste thrills to our diets. Unlike unsprouted beans and other seeds, sprouts need little or no cooking. And germination actually increases certain nutrients in seeds.

During sprouting, seeds are watered regularly for several days to start the growth process. The chemical changes taking place create a tradeoff which is very favorable to human nutrition. Because carbohydrates are burned up to provide the seed with growth energy, sprouts contain a greater proportion of protein and minerals than unsprouted seeds. Moreover, some of the carbohydrates are actually changed into vitamins during sprouting. The Western Regional Research Laboratory of the Agricultural Research Service did a nutritional analysis of four kinds of sprouted seeds and found that in all of them the amount of niacin and vitamin C was greater than before sprouting.

But sprouts are not just a health food. They have gourmet taste. Well over a decade ago, I purchased a small container of alfalfa seed sprouts in a health food store and put them in a salad made up of roughly equal parts of lettuce, tomato, and alfalfa sprouts. A simple vinegar-and-oil dressing was used. The taste was excellent. Nowadays the patrons of the most expensive restaurants are going wild over such salads. And remembering the taste of my first one, I have been a sprout eater ever since, only now I do the sprouting myself.

If you're still doubtful of the place of sprouts in your diet, here is a little piece of inspiration written by Dr. Clive M. McCay, a nutritionist formerly on the staff of Cornell University:

> Our daily paper would surprise us if it carried an ad: "Wanted! a vegetable that will grow in any climate, will rival meat in nutritive value, will mature in three to five days, may be planted any day of the year, will require neither soil nor sunshine, will rival tomatoes in vitamin C, free of waste (in preparation), and which can be cooked with as little fuel and as quickly as a pork chop."

Dr. McCay was talking about the sprouted soybean, which also has good taste.

Many different kinds of seeds can be sprouted and eaten in salads, stews, cereals, breads, casseroles, sandwiches, or as raw snacks or hot vegetable side dishes. Among the seeds suitable for sprouting are alfalfa, barley, buckwheat, cress, fenugreek, flax, garbanzo, lentil, lettuce, lima bean, millet, mung bean, pinto bean, pumpkin, radish, soybean, sunflower, and wheat.

Of course, it isn't necessary to use such a great variety of seeds to get a lot of fun, health, and taste thrills from sprouts. Alfalfa is fine for a delicate taste in salads, and soybeans are the classic for Oriental sprouts. But the mung bean is the best of all and may be the most popular sprout around the world. It is small, so the sprout and the seed are pleasing visually. And the mung bean grows quickly to usable size as a sprout. Usually three days is enough. You can stick with the mung bean and three or four other seeds and do very well.

The basic technique is simplicity itself. Start with clean seeds that have not been treated with fungicides. Health food stores sometimes handle seeds for sprouting, or you can buy lentils or small beans in your local supermarket and use them. Many garden seeds sold by stores or mail-order companies are not chemically treated, but be sure of this if you are going to eat them as sprouts.

Soak the seeds overnight in lukewarm water. Then keep them moist, but not submerged in water, for three to five days. A number of small devices have been made for home seed-sprouting. It is easy to improvise, however. Many people sprout their seeds in mason jars covered with cheesecloth or wire mesh. Others use clean flowerpots and cover the bottom hole with wire mesh. The basic idea is to keep the seeds moist. They should be sprinkled two or three times a day, and kept where the temperature is about 70° Fahrenheit (21° Celsius). It is also necessary for the sprouting seeds to have a certain amount of air so that they won't mold. If you want them to develop green color and some healthful chlorophyll content, expose them to light as they grow.

Sprouts need little preparation before use. I prefer to flush away the green husks of the mung beans, but that's usually all that's needed. Larger, tougher sprouted seeds such as the soybean may be steamed or stir-fried for a few minutes.

One of the best virtues of sprouting as a way to prepare seeds for eating is that it preserves their completeness. Wrapped up in the hard, dry coat of a seed is the universality of life itself. Most of the seeds that are popular foods have a proper balance of minerals, carbohydrates, good-quality protein, and a large quantity of vitamins and oils, too. When primitive people eat seeds, they tend to leave the nutritional balance undisturbed, because they don't have the means to overprocess them. But when advanced, industrialized people eat seeds, they usually get only a part of the nutrition originally contained in them.

The outer coat of rice and wheat is stripped away in our factories, removing much of their mineral and protein value. The germ of the seed, rich in vitamin E, is also taken, so that the food prepared from the grain won't spoil in storage. Nutritionists are finding that people in the advanced countries eat diets that are too low in the very elements milled and processed out of the seeds—calcium, magnesium, and unsaturated fats—all present in the unused part of the seed. By sprouting you can introduce to your diet the whole seed with all its goodness.

Drinking for Health

ere's a prediction. Water is going to be harder to get in the 1980s. More is being used for all purposes, not just drinking. Farmers practicing irrigation are pumping up "fossil water"—the collected rain drops of a million years that aren't being replaced fast enough by today's rains. Whole sections of America's West will feel the pinch when the water table sinks so deep that water can no longer be reached with reasonable energy use. The new synfuel projects require water. So do nuclear plants—for cooling. Just to get enough to drink, we'll soon be forced to use water of even lower quality than we're getting today.

Here's another prediction. The public's lack of concern about what poor-quality water can do to health will soon end—in a flood of publicity about new water-related health discoveries. Whether or not you feel good and live to a ripe age will depend more on the kind of water you can get. Almost everyone will finally realize that basic fact of health, and there'll be a sudden end to the water ignorance we now suffer from.

One final prediction. Soon, water will become one of the best health-building tools. The issue will not be whether water is bad to drink or merely OK. It will be seen more as a big factor in nutrition—not just something to wash clothes with and boil up for tea. You will be able to learn enough about water of extra-good quality to use it to create new and higher levels of health. Mysterious allergies will disappear with the coming of good water. Vague bad feelings will wash away. Cancer rates will drop. Even heart disease may be prevented. The lowering of general water quality will force health-minded people to learn more about their water, and take the steps needed to assure good quality. The waterworks people simply don't care enough—and don't have the money—to do all that must be done to make water pure.

I've been concerned about water quality since 1976, when I wrote two editorials on it for *Prevention*. Digging into the subject then got me all worked up about the junk coming through

American water taps, which includes everything from dead fish to potent cancer-causing chemicals, some actually made during the course of water "purification."

More recently, ominous reports of water supplies contaminated by pesticides and industrial chemicals have begun to appear regularly in the news. But most people are ignoring the implications. According to Carol Keough, who wrote the book *Water Fit to Drink* for Rodale Press:

> *The biggest problem with water today is that the public doesn't really believe there's anything wrong with it. Should tap water develop a bad taste or smell, or an odd color, there's a great outcry. But the really harmful and insidious pollutants usually don't make water taste or smell bad.*
>
> *The general public—and many water treatment folks—still believe chlorination is the solution to any contaminants in water. Not true. We know now that chlorine interacts with naturally found humus and humic acid (in other words, the products of decaying plant matter) to form THM's (trihalomethanes), which are carcinogens. The public is unaware of this. Too bad, since THM's are found in virtually every water supply in this country. Many water utilities seem unruffled by the fact that their standard operating procedure puts a cancer-causing substance into every glass of water we drink.*

What should you do about it? Political pressure on those responsible for water policy is important. Get to your local waterworks people and make sure they know the facts, know that you're watching what they do, and are worried. The amount of chloroform (a THM) actually increases in water after treatment. That's a scandal, which is tolerated only because the public hasn't been alerted to the situation. Water treatment plants are carrying on business as usual.

There are things you can do on your own, even if your local water system is delivering a bad product. One approach is to filter your water through a unit containing activated carbon. In theory, at least, that will chemically grab hold of chloroform as well as other carcinogens. But there has to be enough carbon in the filter to do a good job, and the water must run through the filter slow enough for the filtering effect to take place.

The Environmental Protection Agency has recently completed tests on the effectiveness of some home water filters. The results are not very encouraging. Many of them don't remove enough of the harmful chemical load in water to make their use worthwhile. An exception is the Everpure Model QC4-THM filter, which took out 93 percent of the THM. It uses two filter cartridges, one of granular and the other of powdered carbon.

Larger carbon filters can be made as a do-it-yourself project, or purchased. They are more expensive, and also require the care that should be given all carbon filters. The charge of carbon needs to be changed at exact intervals because bacteria can find a home there.

Distilling your water is another approach. In distillation, water is heated to the boiling point and converted into vapor. That moisture-laden air is converted back into a liquid, and presumably all the impurities—in fact everything other than H_2O—are left behind in the pot in which the water is heated originally. The minerals which give water taste and offer protection against heart disease and other health problems are absent in distilled water. For that reason, some users of stills replace minerals after the process is completed.

Some distilling units may not remove all the carcinogens, though. The problem is that chloroform vaporizes before the boiling point of water is reached, and can pass through the pipe system which converts the heated vapor back into water. A process called fractional distilling prevents that from happening, providing a way to vaporize and carry off the volatile and often harmful chemicals which have a lower boiling point than water. Several home water stills now use the fractional distilling process.

Most people take what they feel is an easier approach to the problem of water purity, and simply buy bottled water for drinking and cooking. They assume that whoever puts the water into the bottles does things to it to make sure it is absolutely pure and good-tasting, or uses water from natural springs that are unpolluted.

Are those assumptions in tune with reality? The Soil and

Health Foundation, a nonprofit research group supported largely by contributions from *Prevention* readers, has tested some of the most popular bottled waters for their mineral content. We have also run taste tests of bottled waters, using Rodale Press staff people as volunteer samplers. The picture that emerges from that multichecking process is not as encouraging as one might hope.

Sodium is part of the problem, particularly with mineral waters like imported Vichy and domestic Saratoga. Vichy was found to have 790.7 parts per million of sodium. One of our testers said it tasted like "salt water." If you're worried about your salt intake, avoid it. Saratoga water, a New York State product, had 541.02 parts per million of sodium. One person said it tasted "like Alka-Seltzer." Years ago the strong taste of these waters apparently made people think they were good medicine. Now we know that salt, which we get too much of, is a big ingredient in that taste. Club soda is also on the salty side, but usually less so than the two bottled waters I mentioned. The brand we tested contained 166.5 parts per million of sodium.

Bacteria can be another worry with bottled water. These products are not chlorinated, which is part of their appeal. Avoiding the effect of chlorine, and its taste, is a prime reason people buy the bottled waters. However, as bad as chlorine is from a taste and THM-producing point of view, it does have the advantage of keeping water low in bacteria while flowing through pipes to your house, or in storage. Bottled water doesn't have that kind of follow-through protection against bacteria buildup. So there have been some cases where water starting out with very low levels of bacteria could build up to troublesome levels by the time it reached your glass. However, I don't want to give the impression that the general run of bottled water is anywhere near as dangerous as tap water. That wouldn't be true.

You should, however, try to make sure the bottled water you drink is not just treated water coming from municipal supplies. According to Dr. Robert Harris of the Environmental Defense Fund, a good choice is spring water from a watershed in a nonindustrialized area. As an added safeguard against bacteria and other pollutants, ask the distributor to give you a signed statement. It should affirm that the water is analyzed at intervals of less than one year and that it has been found free of bacteria, viruses, and metallic and/or organic pollutants. Don't, by the way, drink water in polyvinyl chloride containers. That plastic is cancer-causing and may leach into the bottle's contents.

Despite all the problems, I'm optimistic about water. Once you know how bad the situation is and make the decision to take matters into your own hands, you can find constructive things to do. The issue of adding the mineral fluoride to water to counter tooth decay offers a clear-cut example of how people have fought for water purity when they perceived the threat involved. Government and some medical leaders looked on water as a way to deliver a potent material that could act like a drug on everyone, even those who don't need it. Instead of worrying about the declining quality of water and how that could cause cancer and other serious diseases, local governments began to add one more substance with toxic potential to the thickening chemical soup being delivered to people's homes through city pipes.

Fortunately, many people knew what was happening and applied political pressure to stop the process. In many places the effort failed, but not everywhere, by any means. In hundreds of cities and towns, fluoridation is a nasty word and water is untreated.

Another encouraging sign is that the tools needed to evaluate water and even its effects on health are being improved and are becoming more widely available. For example, the Soil and Health Foundation tests water coming from taps all over the country for seventeen different trace minerals and heavy metals. An analysis of a sample's mineral balance is done at Case Western Reserve University and interpretive information is also supplied.

The results of these tests indicate that about 50 percent of the standing household-water samples tested exceed recommended health limits for some heavy metals or trace minerals. That shows how important it is for you to take charge of your water supply—and not depend entirely on your waterworks. The results of such tests also contribute to a nationwide picture of mineral balance in water, which is useful for research and water-improvement studies.

Water quality also can be assessed indirectly, through tests of mineral levels in the hair. Hair testing is fast becoming a popular service offered by those providing preventative health care, and recent scientific studies have shown that it can reveal that a person has been drinking contaminated water. Lead-poisoning, sometimes a water-related problem, can show up in a hair test. And a recent article in *American Laboratory* tells of a case of arsenic poisoning resulting from water contamination that was discovered by hair testing. According to a study reported in *Environmental Research*, excess selenium in well water has also been confirmed by hair analysis.

Always remember that water flows. It falls as rain in one place, but may travel hundreds or even thousands of miles both above and below ground before it gets to your kitchen sink. Where has it been? Has it flowed past the Love Canal near Buffalo, that infamous industrial chemical dump? Has it trickled through any other of the estimated thirty-two thousand to fifty thousand toxic waste sites which are spotted around the country? Or has it been through the bowels of a large city upstream from you?

We have to ask ourselves questions like that, and try to find the answers. For if we don't, and keep drinking water that is not pure, our efforts to become healthy by improving our nutrition and living healthfully in other ways will be undermined.

3 THE TARGET IS WHOLENESS

Seek Life's Best

Many people have entirely the wrong idea about health. Insurance companies promote "health" insurance when they really mean insurance against the cost of disease. We're bombarded with appeals from voluntary "health" organizations asking for money to conquer heart disease, cancer, birth defects, and so on. The word *health* is used by doctors, hospitals, and drug companies in countless subtle efforts to make us think the best place to find vigor, vitality, and soundness of body is in operating rooms, dispensaries, and drugstores. Those whose function it is to cope with disease have cloaked themselves so completely in the white garments of promoters of health that it is no wonder that the average person fails to see how broad and hopeful the real meaning of health is.

To see health in its true perspective, we should visualize it as a perfect state in the opposite swing of the pendulum from death. Health is complete physical harmony, and death, of course, is the final breakdown of the body. Between those two states are many intermediate qualities and conditions. Close to the state of death are the worst diseases, those that are incurable. Toward the center are accidents and illnesses which will eventually heal. Near the ultimate goal of health we would place the positive qualities of life—balance, harmony, fitness, adventure, faith, love, and wholeness, to mention just a few.

In looking at the whole spectrum of human welfare, you see that disease is only part of the picture. It's one of the barriers that stands in the way of achieving complete health, but not the only one. If we have no disease and have no love, either, can we be healthy? Of course not. Boredom can cause pain and suffering as acute and crippling as many diseases named in medical texts. Would a person seeing no purpose in life be healthier after perceiving a worthwhile goal? Certainly!

Complete health is very difficult to achieve. It may even be out of reach. Rene Dubos, a most perceptive medical philosopher, says that health is a mirage, a utopia that keeps fading as we advance. Because true health is a perfect state and we are not perfect creatures, it is logical to view it as something unattainable. "While it may be comforting to imagine a life free of stresses and strains in a carefree world," wrote Dubos in *The Mirage of Health,* "this will remain an idle dream. Many cannot hope to find another Paradise on earth, because paradise is a static concept while human life is a dynamic process."

Preventing disease is essential to health, but there is no reason why we should be satisfied with freedom from disease and miss the thrill of trying for the highest level of human efficiency, pleasure, and vigor. If we understand clearly the real meaning of health—and the challenge it offers to us—healthful living can become an adventure and a source of great pleasure. By trying to be truly healthy we can find a wholeness and harmony in life that is far beyond the reach of the average person.

Each advance in our level of health should be looked on as an opportunity to live life more thoroughly. If you have been overweight and get your body into an attractive shape through diet, start enjoying your new figure! Do the things that you hesitated to do before because you were fat. If your sensible diet pays off in increased energy and resistance to disease, use your new vim to widen your horizons. Try harder to advance in your job, to enjoy your hobbies, to make new friends. A fitness program can also lead to new joys and experiences, if you look on exercise not as an end in itself but as a gateway to pleasures and achievements formerly out of reach. A person who seeks health only for the sake of saying he or she is healthy may miss many of the joys of life that are easily attainable.

It's most important to realize that many of the things you can do if you are healthy are more than just rewards for good living. They are stepping-stones to even better levels of health. When you start to build health the constructive way, you direct your life into a positive cycle of action leading to greater strength, vitality, peace of mind, and general satisfaction. Each improvement leads to another. If you start eating whole, natural foods that are rich in vitamins and minerals, you will have done more than just protect yourself against nutritional deficiencies. You will also feel better, and you will be more ready to exercise, to travel, to take on new challenges. If you stop smoking, not only will you have less risk of getting cancer and heart disease, you will breathe easier and have more confidence in your ability to control your own destiny. If you walk an hour daily, you'll do more than strengthen your legs. Blood will flow strongly through your body, your appearance will begin to improve, and your mind will be ready to focus on the tasks you have to face.

Here is a good way to visualize health. Picture yourself standing on an island in the middle of the river of life. One shore of the river is health, the other is death. Between the island and either shore are many stepping-stones, each representing a practice that will help either to improve or to destroy your health. Each is labeled. If you turn and face the shore of death, you will see stones labeled "sedentary living," "poor diet," and so forth. Toward the shore of health are the stones of "refreshing rest," "love," "adventure," "good food," "vitamins," "recreation," and so on.

It is up to you to decide the direction you wish to travel. If you head toward the shore of health, you may step first on the stone of "good food." From there you might go on to "satisfying work" and then to "esthetic experience." Someone else might chart a different route to the health shore, starting perhaps on "refreshing rest" and going next to "vitamins." Although all the attributes of health are important, some are more vital than others. So in this idealized picture of life we should think of the more important stepping-stones, such as "good food," as being bigger than others and on a more direct route to the health shore. No matter which route you travel, if you step on as many of the good stones as possible you will get closer to the shore of health. The direction is most important, not necessarily the exact route. If you head in the right direction, it is easier to step on more of the right stones.

Most people seem unable to decide in which direction to go. They just wade downstream, stepping on good stones and on bad ones. But to get from a bad stone to a good one is difficult, because to do that you have to cross the river of life at the center, the swiftest and deepest part. Of course, there is a time for each of us when the river rises to flood stage, and everything gets swept away. But if in our youth or middle years we set out toward the healthy shore, we will have reached many exciting and pleasurable stopping points before the flood. And if the flood is not a very big one, we will be close enough to the health shore to be able to hold on until the flood subsides.

How many stepping-stones are there? It may surprise you how many you can reach. Health is the product of many complex factors working together. It's important to start with a good hereditary background and to grow up and live in a clean, pure environment. An adequate standard of living is significant, as are good nutrition, ample vitamins and minerals, refreshing rest, and defense against frustration. Boredom is a negative factor in the good health equation, and stress can be, too. Love, recreation, and esthetic experiences are important, as is the opportunity for adventure and the taking of risks. Ideals, values, spiritual faith, a will to live, and a search for the meaning of life contribute to health. It is necessary to have a job that rewards you adequately, and not simply with money. You need good medical care when disease or accident strikes. You need a good level of physical fitness. Perhaps you can add your own items, qualities or conditions which help make you healthy.

To step back to the beginning for a moment, our goal is health, the best in life. We have both a good opportunity and an interesting obligation to "take our health into our own hands." We have the opportunity because many of the contagious diseases—which plagued people in past generations—are much less of a problem.

For example, a look at the *Statistical Abstract of the United States* for 1979 will tell you that in 1977 only 2.7 percent of all American deaths were caused by pneumonia or influenza, both once major killers. On the other hand, fully 60 percent of those dying in 1977 were the victims of major cardiovascular diseases or cerebrovascular disease and another 20 percent died of malignancies—all health problems that can be countered or even prevented by choices we ourselves make. As the assistant director for public health practice of the Centers for Disease Control—Dr. Donald Miller—has pointed out, we have reached the stage where any future gains in life expectancy will have to come from changes in our habits and lifestyles.

So to live a healthy, rewarding, and long life, we are today challenged by circumstances to pull ourselves up by our bootstraps. Heart disease is a good illustration of the role of personal choices in health. Whether or not we are candidates for heart attacks depends on things that we do freely to ourselves. They include habits of smoking, eating, exercise, and rest.

Many of the commoner forms of cancer are also strongly influenced by life choices. At an international symposium on cancer in autumn of 1980, Dr. Michael Shimkin of the University of California at Los Angeles was among the speakers. After studying cancer-causing agents in social and industrial settings for over twenty-five years, this expert has found that "the influence of industrial cancers is very small in relationship to the lifestyle cancers." Citing a recent study that suggests urban living somehow contributes to susceptibility of cancer, Dr. Shimkin noted that "there appears to be something in the totality of congestion of human beings—so-called advanced living conditions—that makes people more vulnerable to cancer." In her recent book *Preventing Cancer* (1978, W. W. Norton, New York), epidemiologist Elizabeth Whelan is more specific. She reports that up to 50 percent of the cancers in women and 30 percent of those in men "are the result of imprudent diet." According to Dr. Whelan, the problem may be diets that are deficient in protective nutrients, diets that contain cancer-causing agents, or diets excessively rich in fat and cholesterol, which are now believed to overstimulate the hormone system and so contribute to the development of breast, bowel, and prostate cancer.

Cigarette smoking is also a key culprit, causing 85 percent of all lung cancers and 53.9 percent of all cancers of the mouth. There is evidence that alcohol consumption also increases the chance of cancer at body sites such as the esophagus, the liver, and the larynx, with smoking compounding the risk.

Even the decision to get a deep tan each summer affects cancer chances, for the sun has been called "the most universal carcinogen." Overexposure is linked to the deadly skin cancer melanoma, which is now one of the most rapidly increasing forms of cancer among white Americans.

In many ways, then, now more than ever we can choose our destiny. If we can somehow master the strength of will and purpose to do the right things, we have today the best chance ever to live a long, healthy, and productive life. On the other hand, if we view health only as the absence of disease—and don't perceive the challenge of building strength and vigor in a positive sense—we become sitting ducks for the degenerative diseases which strike down more people every year. It is possible to seem healthy to yourself, and even to your physician, while the deposits leading to heart attack build up. This process begins early in life in America—in one study done in Iowa about 70 percent of the young people from six to eighteen had the beginnings of heart disease. Cancer cells also can grow undiscovered for many years before calling attention to themselves via physical symptoms.

The absence of overt sickness is simply no longer a valid index of health. Health is much more than the absence of disease. It is the ability to find superior powers of body and mind and to use them for full, fruitful, and enjoyable living. Disease is a barrier, but it is only a barrier. We must go far beyond thoughts of illness or absence of illness to get the most out of life. The best we can do is to travel as many of the right stepping-stones in the river of life as possible.

Can Money Buy Health?

People who seek health in doctors' offices or hospitals frequently return home disappointed. That's because the amount of money spent on health care is not directly related to how healthy we are or to how long we live. In the United States the latest available figures (for 1978) peg our total health care costs at over $192 billion a year, and the average expense for one day in the hospital at $222.

Despite this staggering investment, Americans do not live significantly longer than other peoples. In terms of ranking, the United States is only number ten in the world for length of life.

Not only has our enormous health care establishment failed to extend our lives significantly—it may actually be shortening them. The problem is that in a medically oriented society, doctors thrive financially only when there is a lot of sickness. And they are better paid for intervening than for not intervening. Social critic Ivan Illich wrote about this sad state of affairs several years ago in *Medical Nemesis: The Expropriation of Health.* Just one of the telling points he made was that in such a system doctors are likely to undertake aggressive treatment even when there is no proof that good results will lengthen life expectancy or make the patient more comfortable. And consequently, many operations performed are unnecessary.

More recently, a respected member of the medical establishment has been making the same case against his colleagues. In a book called *Confessions of a Medical Heretic,* Dr. Robert Mendelsohn wryly notes that surgery is often scheduled not because of the condition of the patient, but because our country now has a surplus of surgeons—a full forty thousand more than the American College of Surgeons says would be sufficient.

A nationally syndicated medical columnist, Dr. Mendelsohn reports that by *conservative* estimate, about 2.4 million unnecessary operations are performed each year, resulting in the loss of twelve thousand lives. Hospitalized patients also may become sicker or even die because of poor reactions to drug therapy or diagnostic procedures—or because they come down with a hospital-acquired infection. According to Dr. Mendelsohn, our chances of getting sick in the hospital are one in twenty, and such infections kill about fifteen thousand people annually.

Even if we escape unneeded surgery and hospital-caused diseases, we may, says Dr. Mendelsohn, be treated on the basis of laboratory tests that produce false information. Or fall victim to any other of a host of human errors or accidents occurring in hospitals.

It seems, then, that for at least some of us, health may be negatively linked to the amount of money we spend trying to attain it. Dr. Mendelsohn, for one, firmly believes that if 90 percent of the doctors, drugs, hospitals, and equipment of "modern medicine" were to vanish, "the effect on our health would be immediate and beneficial."

But suppose we assume that all medical care is of the very highest quality. Even so, it's possible that nothing significant can be done medically to lengthen human life. British gerontologist Alex Comfort is of the opinion that in getting us through to our seventies medicine has just about "shot its bolt." In a book on growing old called *A Good Age*, he notes that "there is little chance that the cure of further diseases on a one-off basis will greatly extend our lives." Even curing heart disease, stroke, and cancer—which now account for 80 percent of deaths in the United States—would add only about seven years to overall life expectancy here and only about 2½ years to the life span of someone sixty-five years old. That's because, says Comfort, in really old people there are likely to be twelve or thirteen causes of possible death.

Clearly, it will be easier to achieve greater health by changing cultural factors than by throwing more money at the medical establishment. For example, just two of our more popular habits, smoking cigarettes and drinking alcohol, have been linked to two-thirds of all the disease in our country. From 1950 to 1977 the number of deaths from lung cancer per one hundred thousand

Americans jumped by over 2½ times. That happened despite the fact that better techniques of lung surgery have been developed and that treatment of cancer itself has improved. Such breakthroughs in technology just couldn't cope with the public's greater self-exposure to cigarette smoke. For although the number of male smokers has leveled off during the past decade, more women are acquiring the habit. As a result, the 1980 Surgeon General's report predicts that the female death rate from lung cancer of the early 1960s will quadruple by 1983.

Another controllable cultural factor affecting health and longevity is automobile accidents. A lot of people are going to be injured or killed in automobile accidents unless engineers develop safer cars and highways and people make more intelligent use of the safety devices available to them and become more willing to save gas—and lives—by respecting 55 mph speed limits. We'll also have to stop mixing drinking with driving, for alcohol is involved in half of the nearly fifty thousand annual deaths on our roads.

Yes, health comes more and more from the way people live and not from doctors and hospitals. Even during the heyday of infectious diseases, it was doubtful whether the health status of a community was primarily determined by the quality and quantity of its medical services. For instance, tuberculosis started to decline in the United States long before modern drugs and new therapies were used to treat the disease. When people started living in a manner unsuited to tuberculosis, they stopped getting the disease.

The same fate could befall half of the ten current leading causes of death in the United States—coronary artery disease, dominant forms of cancer, stroke, general arteriosclerosis, and diabetes. All of these major health problems are strongly influenced by the way we live, and they can only be delayed or mitigated by modern medicine. Stopping them in their tracks will require a basic change in the ecology of this country—not outrageously inflated outlays in money for technological research and health care.

National Health Insurance—Milestone or Millstone?

mericans are likely to find out the hard way just how little wealth and health have to do with each other if national health insurance ever becomes a reality. Every other industrialized nation has it, in one form or another. Americans want it, according to opinion polls. Legislation to establish it has been kicking around Capitol Hill for many years and versions of such a plan seem certain to come before Congress sooner or later. A major milestone—health care based upon need, rather than ability to pay—is about to be chiseled and set in place. But will national health insurance really be a milestone for preventive medicine?

Imagine this ideal scenario: the federal government, as the future payer of all medical bills, finally is forced to realize that an ounce of prevention costs far less than a pound of cure. It would give tax breaks to health food stores; sponsor community recreation and exercise; curb advertising that encourages abuse of food, tobacco, and alcohol; mandate plain-English food labeling, and drive the toxins from our homes and workplaces, from the air we breathe, and from the water we drink.

It would mandate nutritional training for doctors and preparers of institutional food. Finally, it would pay for holistic health therapies that it currently refuses to reimburse under Medicare and Medicaid.

In a word, it would make health care focus on health.

Now let's look at the "hard-nosed realist" scenario. If the past is prologue, then the federal government couldn't possibly buck all the vested interests necessary to make such changes. Nor would it want to, given its aversion to foresight and leadership.

So health care would continue to focus on sickness—with a vengeance.

Under the banner of "cost control," it would declare what treatments are "proper," and propriety would be determined by the medical establishment. If you wanted to be treated with herbs, vitamins, or yoga before resorting to drugs, you would have to pay for it yourself, in addition to paying taxes for the drug treatments of others. Hospitals and doctors' offices would be glutted with imaginary invalids and those who don't think about their own health because the government will patch them up.

People who keep healthy would have to pay even more for the treatment of those who refuse to take care of themselves.

In short, national health insurance would be a millstone around the neck of innovative medicine.

It has become fashionable to mouth the words *preventive medicine* when discussing national health insurance. They are sounded with reverence in public hearings and newspaper editorials, in the halls of Congress and the pronouncements of presidents.

"Preventive medicine" makes a fine political refrain because it conjures up the old adage of fiscal prudence, and the speakers aren't pressed to explain further. Great rhetoric, by definition. But what do they mean? Annual checkups? Swine flu shots? Clean latrines?

If annual checkups are what the proponents of preventive medicine have in mind, they're in for disappointment. So often, a checkup tells you one of two things: (1) you've been taking care of yourself, or (2) you haven't. "What we have in America today is an epidemic of degenerative disease," says Garry F. Gordon, M.D., a California physician and chairman of the board of the American Academy of Medical Preventics. With our high blood pressure and our cholesterol counts, "virtually anyone after 40 can be documented as having coronary artery disease."

If a disease has got hold of you, the doctor may be able to help, and then again he may not. "The sooner you see a physician and get diagnosed as having cancer, the sooner you die," because of the brutal effect of chemotherapy, says Dr. Gordon. "There are strong statistics to back that up. Conventional medicine has nothing to offer for most cancers."

This, in the face of the boxcars of money being wheeled into the health care system, makes some people say we shouldn't spend one more dollar on disease. Herbert Denenberg, former Pennsylvania insurance commissioner, now a consumer editor for Philadelphia media and member of the Institute of Medicine of the National Academy of Sciences, has declared, "When you view the gross inefficiency of the federal government and the health care system, any money spent on prevention has to give you a better return on the dollar."

Well said . . . but easier said than done. The problem is that "prevention requires working with people, because in some ways you go against what people think they should be getting," says Harold S. Luft, Ph.D., an associate professor of health economics at the University of California at San Francisco. According to Dr. Luft, Americans expect the same kind of high-technology treatments being shown on TV medical dramas.

Prevention in place of wonder drugs and million-dollar equipment not only spoils the fun of these shows, it spoils the fun of our bad habits. To be lazy and self-indulgent is human nature. Assuming that inclination will continue into the foreseeable future, national health insurance could subtly undermine personal prevention. "It might be argued that a government which encourages us to put total responsibility for our health into its hands could end by making us even less responsible for our own health." The writer: former Secretary of the Treasury William Simon, in the *American Spectator*.

In addition to those who are sick because it's their own fault, those who aren't sick at all could become an increasing burden on the medical system. These patients—with their vague aches, "lack of pep," or "blahs" that have origins beyond the physical realm of diagnosis and treatment—are right now sitting in doctors' offices everywhere.

And what do you suppose will happen when supposedly "free" medical care comes along? "It will be like offering free airplane tickets to London," says Dr. Gordon. "Everyone wants the system to get them well, and frankly the system can't do it."

You already know how America pays through the nose for sickness: it's the nation's third largest industry; it snatches up one dollar in every twelve. Between 1965 and 1979 its cost rose more than twice as fast as prices in general. Chiefly responsible is the skyrocketing cost of hospitalization. More than coincidentally, 92 percent of hospital bills are not paid directly by consumers, but by insurance companies and the government. In effect, hospitals are given a blank check for "the best treatment that money can buy." Whether you need it or not.

You also know the government's pitiful track record in controlling these costs. Look at the prototypes of national health insurance already in place: Medicare for the elderly, Medicaid for the poor. Catastrophes, both. Since they came "on line," the overall price of medicine has quadrupled. Fraudulent billing of these programs has hit the headlines and doctors have been indicted, but that's only a small part of the total escalation. Federal, state, and local taxes paying for health care in 1965 were $9.5 billion, or 25 percent of total medical spending. In 1978 the outlay was $78.1 billion, or 41 percent of the total.

Figures aside, bear in mind one thing: nobody thought this would happen. When Medicaid was proposed to Congress in the 1960s, the cost of federal spending was estimated at $258 million annually. What was once said in earnest is now a farce.

In the throes of this awakening, did the government try to reduce the cost of its medical bills by breaking new ground in prevention? Not a bit. Instead of innovation, it attempted something that is, in its effect, the opposite: standardization. It set up Peer Standard Review Organizations (PSROs) to approve hospital treatments billed to the federal government.

Whether PSROs have been effective in reducing overtreatment, waste, and fraud is a much-debated topic. What is crystal clear is this: PSROs won't approve payment for natural healing methods, even though those methods are far less costly than conventional care. Rather than broadening our medical horizons, the government has encouraged a limited version of health practice by defining what it considers to be "acceptable medical treatment."

The irony of it all—that the government gives exclusive

patronage to the very crisis-oriented brand of medicine responsible for the high cost of health treatment and the absence of health.

Under national health insurance, it will be even more of the old saw, "he who pays, controls," says Dr. Gordon. "They're going to be telling physicians what they may or may not prescribe and when to start and stop treatment. There are always those kinds of problems when you standardize, and if you don't standardize, you can't control costs."

What are the chances that national health insurance would recognize holistic health treatment? Mighty slim. "Nothing the government will ever embrace will be anything but mainstream," says Dr. Gordon. That's the nature of the beast.

Now for the silver lining on this story: there is a state health insurance plan that is in the process of recognizing vitamin and mineral therapy. California has recently completed a three-county pilot program called Medi-Cal. Medi-Cal clients were reimbursed for the whole gamut of nutritional treatment, including vitamins, minerals, special dietary regimes, nutritional counseling, glucose tolerance tests, and hair tests (to detect absences of trace elements in the body). After the results of the three pilot counties have been evaluated, the decision will be made as to whether the program will become statewide policy.

Could a similar bill ever get through Congress? Could it make its way past the lobbying power and establishment stance of the American Medical Association? It's worth a try, and now is the time, while national health insurance is up for debate. Recognition and support for holistic therapies, and for truly preventive measures as well, ought to happen in tandem with any expansion of health care.

Otherwise, our future national health insurance will be thumbing its nose at health.

What Health Fix
Do *You* Want?

In the minds of most people the good sound of the name preventive medicine is reinforced by its history of controlling certain diseases. Polio is hardly a problem today, thanks to preventive medicine programs. Smallpox is on the verge of being wiped out in the world, because of successful inoculation systems. Yellow fever is no longer much of a worry, if you get your shots.

Yet if you look beyond those medical battles won, you still see people around the world who are mighty sick. There is in fact a vast reservoir of sickness. It almost seems that when one disease is controlled another becomes more vigorous and takes its place. Here in the United States we keep building more hospitals, training more doctors and nurses, making more drugs, and using all those medical resources more vigorously than before. The cost of all this so-called health effort is rising rapidly, to the point where it threatens to bankrupt even well-to-do people within a few years. Preventive medicine has failed to protect us.

Why should that be? Is this health disaster impending because we have not devoted enough resources to preventive medicine? The answer to that question is a resounding no! We have in fact been confused into thinking that preventive medicine is the answer to health problems, when it actually isn't the answer and in many cases itself becomes the problem.

That was the case with the massive swine flu inoculation program which resulted in the paralysis of some of those participating. Maybe things would have been different if swine flu really had spread through our population in a dangerous form. I will concede that much. But I think we can gain far more real health in the long run if we look at this abortive program as the failure that it was, instead of as the success that it might have been.

The lesson we should learn from that fiasco is that preventive medicine is too limited in its theory and practice because it relies to a very large extent on the technical fix. The primary preventive medicine approach to a health problem is to seek a technical solution that will eliminate or control the potential disease process without changing the lifestyle of the people subject to the disease. Many times the people so treated have no understanding of what has happened, except that they have been inoculated. Sometimes the technical fix is put on people without them even knowing it. For example, if enough people in a population group take the oral Sabin live-virus polio vaccine, others in the community who have not taken it will also be protected. Fluoridation of water to prevent dental decay is another technical fix of preventive medicine. And not everyone who drinks fluoridated water knows that the water has been treated.

The technical fix has been used by preventive medicine practitioners primarily against infectious disease. The idea works better there. In infectious disease, an organism or group of organisms is at large in the population. It is studied carefully by scientists, who find out what it is, how it spreads, when it is likely to become virulent, and what antibodies are created by the body to defend against it. Then, using the best available technical methods, a vaccine or other system to counter that organism is created and used.

When used carefully and not touted as the golden road to real health, the technical fix has its place in a disease-prevention system. But what has actually happened is that the fix has worked so well against very dramatic diseases, like yellow fever and polio, that it has been promoted heavily as the major approach to health. People have been led to believe that sooner or later every health problem will be fixed in that way, as long as they are willing to roll up their sleeves and present their arms to be inoculated. That is a wrong idea, for every technical fix is likely to backfire someday, in some way.

That happens because our natural world is a tightly interconnected web of organisms and substances. It is virtually impossible to manipulate or "fix" one without causing a disruption somewhere else in the web. And that disruption can indeed be very serious.

We can see how that actually happens by comparing the technical-fix approach to a health problem with what I call the natural fix. Usually, the natural fix is very simple, has far less chance of backfiring, and is inexpensive. The natural fix involves people directly in the prevention of their health problems. It requires that they be educated so that they know what is happening, what might happen later, and can take steps to alter their lifestyle in ways that will make them healthier. We'll start with a couple of technical fixes for accidental hazards.

Burns. Ways are now available to apply chemicals to cloth to make it fire resistant. There is a federal law requiring such fire retardant treatment of clothing for infants. That is the technical fix.

How does that fix backfire? First, recent studies show that the chemical used to make infant clothes fire resistant is a mutagen. Because the chemical can be absorbed through the skin, there's a possibility that it can cause cancer or genetic damage. That puts parents on the horns of a dilemma. They can protect their child from fire now, but perhaps expose him or her to cancer later.

Another backfire of this technical fix is that fire retardant chemicals, as a general class, can be very toxic to the environment. People in Michigan discovered that a few years ago, when a shipment of polybrominated biphenyl (PBB), used as a fire retardant, was inadvertently mixed into animal feed. Being very toxic and also resistant to breakdown, PBB has literally contaminated all of Michigan and caused serious health problems. It is now reported to have spread into the food supply and environment of thirteen other states.

Caffeine Sensitivity. Drinking coffee and tea causes many people to suffer from a caffeine reaction. They become nervous, can't sleep, and sometimes have other health problems related to caffeine intake. The technical fix here is to make decaffeinated coffee. That used to be done by flushing the coffee beans with trichloroethylene (TCE), a solvent that is also used in dry cleaning and for degreasing machine parts.

Not surprisingly, in the mid-1970s, the National Cancer Institute issued an alert about the possibly toxic residues from this chemical, which has been found to cause cancer in mice. After that, most manufacturers of decaffeinated coffee switched to methylene chloride, another chlorinated hydrocarbon solvent. Everyone expects that this one, too, will be banned eventually when tests on it are completed. But United States companies are still reluctant to use the pure water processing method perfected and introduced last year by a Swiss firm. And so the only Americans now drinking decaffeinated coffee without solvent residues in it are those who buy certain imported "decaf" beans at specialty and gourmet food shops.

But even the safest technical fix may not curb caffeine consumption. One study indicates that people subconsciously subvert the decaffeinating process by drinking greater amounts of that kind of coffee. They keep drinking until they get the caffeine they crave. That work was done at Wesleyan University in Middletown, Connecticut, by Lynn T. Kozlowski.

The natural fix for caffeine-caused health problems is obvious. Simply teach yourself to like another beverage, such as herb tea or even plain water.

Drugs. The range of technical fixes in the form of medications is almost unending, and so are the backfires. Almost every single drug or medicine in common use has at least one harmful side effect, and often more than one. While many drugs are potential lifesavers, it also goes without question that most sick people recover because of the natural disease-fighting mechanism within their own bodies, not because of the action of drugs they are given.

Let's consider just a few classes of drugs. The use of tranquilizers is the common technical fix for nervousness, anxiety, and stressful situations. Tranquilizers work, but they are expensive and tend to make people dependent on a chemical crutch. Perhaps most important, the use of these drugs causes people not to face up to the aspects of their lifestyle which are making them untranquil. In fact, their masking of the causes of anxiety can lead people to blunder into more stress or even outright danger. Perhaps thousands of accidents are caused each year by people under the influence of tranquilizers.

Natural fixes for simple anxiety and nervous problems can

be found. Exercise can be a big help. A long walk will often do far more good than a packet of pills. Some people are making themselves nervous by eating foods they are allergic to, or by taking in too much caffeine or sugar, which are affecting their brain and blood chemistry. For them a change in diet can be a big help. Even a hot bath has an important calming effect—and no side effects. And bedtime snacks of foods containing natural relaxants such as calcium or the amino acid tryptophan can assure restful sleep without a bad reaction the next day.

Antibiotics present an even more interesting example of the danger of the technical fix than tranquilizers. To start with, there's some question whether antibiotics really are as effective as people think they are. Certainly, lives have been saved by antibiotics. But as I suggested earlier in regard to tuberculosis, declines in mortality from infectious diseases reported in Western countries could well be the result of other causes.

"Antibiotics and chemotherapeutic drugs have not had the dramatic effect on the mortality of infectious diseases popularly attributed to them," say Elina Hemminki, M.D., and Anneli Paakkulainen in the *American Journal of Public Health*. In a careful statistical study, it was discovered that deaths in Sweden and Finland from ten important infectious diseases had started going down well before antibiotics came on the scene, and the rate of mortality didn't change when antibiotics began to be used.

C. T. Stewart, writing in the *Journal of Human Resources*, reported similar statistics and pointed more directly to a natural fix as the cause of declining deaths. Stewart found that widespread literacy and access to clean water were the main factors in increasing life spans in Western countries, and claimed that medical treatments did not have a significant effect.

Antibiotics do affect disease organisms, though, we have found to our sorrow. When overused, as is so common today, they can cause bacteria to evolve into more resistant forms. Then, the antibiotic involved is no longer able to control disease caused by that bacteria.

Vaccines. The greatest preventive medicine success of all time is the elimination of smallpox, a disease which has plagued mankind for thousands of years. That is the ultimate technical fix of medical science. Can it backfire, as I have said all such fixes will?

The backfire has already occurred for some people. Thousands have died because of reactions to the smallpox vaccine.

Now that the disease is just about totally wiped out, are we safe from it? I'm not sure. Over the next few generations, the immunity to smallpox that has been built up by vaccination programs will dissipate. In fifty to seventy years, there will be billions of people who are not immune to smallpox. Should the disease reappear, they would be endangered.

Yet the virus will still exist, maintained in frozen form for research purposes in about a dozen laboratories around the world. Is it too far out to imagine that some of that virus could be released and spread, either accidentally or deliberately? Few people are aware of these potential problems.

Right there is one of the basic difficulties with preventive medicine. The successes are glorified, and the failures or problems minimized. There is glamour in wiping out a disease. Yet thousands have died of vaccination complications, with hardly anyone noticing.

All that changed with the swine flu debacle, which exposed the technical medical fix as a clever manipulation of human biology with a big potential for success, but perhaps an even bigger potential for failure. Everyone was distressed at what happened to the unfortunate victims of the swine flu program. But we should keep in mind that even worse things could happen in the future. The legacy of some future technical fix could be the release of a supermonster into our midst—or even a series of supermonsters.

John McKinlay, a Boston University sociologist who works primarily in areas of health policy, puts the blame for this kind of risk on what he calls "the medical-industrial complex." He says that despite all the apparently successful preventive medicine programs, there remains a vast "illness iceberg" made up of people with hidden sickness, who aren't being helped by conventional medicine. In fact, he says that this medical-industrial complex "actually manufactures illness, then erects an expensive, ineffective medical system to care for the sick, and finally profits even further from illness by producing costly goods and services to keep that system running."

Those are rough words, but one of McKinlay's suggestions for action is even more blunt.

"Maybe we need to educate the population to shy away from medicine, develop healthy lifestyles, and make it on their own," he said recently. "Maybe independent behavior is healthy behavior. Maybe self-help is more effective than professional help."

In effect, he is suggesting that we make more and better use of the natural fix, and less use of the technical fix. One way of starting to do that is to take a hard look at our love affair with energy. That infatuation has fueled many of the technological excesses that are sabotaging our health.

Preventing Energy Disease

Energy is dynamic. Using it does things to you. You can create health or sickness for yourself by managing the energy that flows into and around yourself in different ways.

Healthful management of your energy flow is largely a personal matter, but energy decisions are also shaped by the policies and attitudes of the country in which you live. America has been on an energy binge for the past hundred years. Because so much fuel and electricity are used, many people have gotten into the habit of not using fully the energy potential that is in their own bodies. The average person can go through life doing hardly any physical work at all. Almost every routine task is mechanized.

We used to think of our energy-rich way of life as a supreme value. In no other country did the average person have such big cars, totally powered homes, and other signs of energy luxury. That was good for us, we thought. Now, when paying for all that energy is becoming difficult, we aren't so sure of the rightness of the high-energy American way.

People outside America seem to see more clearly than we what these stupendous energy flows have done to the health of our country. "The United States has expanded to be a fat man with a lot of fat on its back." That comment was made a few years ago by Deng Xiao-ping, then the vice premier of China. He looked inside the gloss of our richness and saw a soggy, soft core. His country is much poorer than ours, but in a collective sense it is lean. If there is a disruption in the world's energy flows, the health of China will not be affected drastically. Our fat economy would wither quickly if people in only a few other countries decided to stop catering to our energy gluttony.

The insides of people are changed by too much energy in the same way. In fact, the diseases of civilization are actually a form of energy sickness. They happen when a society has available for its use more energy than it knows how to apply in healthful ways.

Many of the illnesses which commonly afflict people living in advanced countries are rare or even nonexistent among people living in less developed places. A disease of civilization is usually not infectious. You get it not by coming in contact with some germ, but by living for many years in a place where a supposedly high standard of living gradually undermines the integrity of your bodily structure. Dysentery, malaria, schistosomiasis, and similar illnesses are not diseases of civilization, because they can either be prevented by good sanitation, or simply don't occur in the temperate regions where most advanced countries are located.

Heart disease, diabetes, emphysema, and many forms of cancer are different. They are major health problems here, but are often almost totally absent in poorer countries. For years, many doctors thought we got those chronic, degenerative diseases (and poorer peoples didn't) because they tend to crop up during the later years of life. People in underdeveloped countries don't live long enough to get them, or don't have medical service good enough to diagnose them, we were told.

More sophisticated studies then began to show a different picture. Dr. Denis Burkitt's work with fiber in the diet of rural

Africans revealed that they rarely got cancer of the colon, no matter how long they lived. Similar research showed that high blood pressure never occurs where native people exercise, stay thin, and avoid eating salt. We know now that there is also very little hardening of the arteries among people living in many desperately poor underdeveloped countries, while plaque deposits begin to clog the arteries of young children in America, and heart attacks can strike people here in their twenties.

Clearly, things that are unseen and undetected for many years happen to people when they live in an advanced, high-energy country. Almost always they are not good for a person's health and result eventually in disease that is extremely serious and chronic. The nibbling away at a person's inner structure which results in a heart attack or cancer during the mature years almost never can be reversed by medication, and even the most advanced and expensive operations usually give only a short reprieve.

What we need desperately is more understanding of why diseases of civilization occur. It isn't enough just to say to people that they should live naturally, avoid food additives and junk food, exercise regularly, get enough sleep, and improve their nutrition. They need to know why the kind of lifestyle that is accepted as normal here, and even thought to be especially good, is really doing them in. That's why the concept of looking at how and where energy flows into your life can be so valuable.

First of all, we can see that the amount of energy used in developed countries like ours is almost astronomically greater than the energy use of underdeveloped countries. Let's consider China as an example. There are almost a billion people in China, yet that country uses in total—for all purposes—the amount of energy the United States uses just for air-conditioning. A whole Chinese village, and maybe even a small town, gets along on the energy budget of one large American house.

The heart disease rate in China is much lower than it is here. Energy plays a role in that difference, because the factors in our more advanced way of life that weaken our hearts require big energy inputs. We get little exercise compared to the Chinese. Whereas they walk or ride bicycles, Americans consume oil or electricity to get around. Too, the Chinese diet is much lower in fat than ours. The production of butter, lard, fatty meats, and edible oils is very energy intensive, and farmers and food processors use up much nonrenewable energy producing the fatty foods which are typically American. A low-fat diet based more on whole grain cereals and leafy vegetables grown locally could be produced with much less energy. And if people here ate that kind of fiber-rich, natural diet, diseases of civilization would be avoided.

Let's look more closely at food processing. Highly refined white flour is a hallmark of the civilized life in developed countries. Converting wheat grain into that kind of flour takes much more energy than does grinding wheat into whole grain flour. The process is much simpler, and less wheat is used to make a pound of whole wheat flour than a pound of white flour. If people ate only whole wheat flour, they would have a diet richer in fiber and important vitamins and minerals, and would be insulating themselves from intestinal disease as well as other problems common in developed countries. Thinking of whole grain foods as being low-energy products can give you an important extra reason for eating them.

Noise is another important factor. We know now that in addition to causing immediate nervous problems, loud intrusions on daily life undermine basic health in gradual ways. For example, high blood pressure is significantly related to heart disease and other degenerative diseases. And in a study of the health records of a Maryland shipbuilding firm, it was found that workers laboring in the noisiest parts of the yard for five years or more were six times more likely to have seriously elevated blood pressure than those working in quieter areas. Now, no aspect of life in a developed country is more closely related to energy use than is noise. Without fuel, there simply is no way to make the kind and amount of noise that is so troubling to people today.

Another example is fatness. Of all the diseases of civilization, none is more closely related to excess and wrong use of energy than is obesity. People living in advanced countries, particularly the United States, are much fatter on the average than are Chinese, Indians, Africans, and various native peoples who avoid many of our disease problems. You can see that difference in weight with your own eyes by traveling in less developed countries.

Major causes of fatness here are directly related to excess energy use. People wouldn't be so fat if they walked more and rode in cars less. They wouldn't be so fat if they were less subject to noise, tensions, and other irritations that are common in a high-energy country. Such stress causes many of us to use food and drink as a form of relief from the frenetic pressures of the day, rather than as a source of right nourishment.

Fatness would also be less common if, as I said before, our food production system were based on more local production of vegetables and other natural foods, and if people ate less of the energy-intensive snacks and processed foods which are so rich in fat, salt, sugar, and other simple carbohydrates.

There is another side of the coin. Much energy could be saved if fat people would eat less. Tim Lohman, Ph.D., of the Physical Fitness Research Lab at the University of Illinois, and Bruce M. Hannon, Ph.D., director of the Energy Research Group at that university, studied the situation and concluded that fat people in America are eating so much extra food that they're creating a drain on our energy stores.

Their survey showed that in 1975 American men were carrying 850 million more pounds of fat than they should, and women had 1.5 billion pounds of excess fat. A lot of energy was used to produce, market, and prepare the food they ate. So, if all those overweight people would reduce their weight to normal, Dr. Hannon computed, the reduction in food needs would translate into a saving of 1/10 of 1 percent of all energy used in the United States. If that doesn't sound like much to you, think of it this way. That amount of energy would keep nine hundred thousand typical autos fueled each year.

The real tragedy, though, is that all the extra fat many people carry around gets in the way of their generating the one kind of energy that is totally useful to them—their own. Here is the most important part of my message. Energy that comes into your life from outside has to be managed with extreme care to keep it from hurting your health. But the energy you generate inside yourself by eating well and moving vigorously through life can improve your health. To avoid the illnesses of civilization, I believe, we have to clear our heads of the old idea that an effortless, push-button society will make possible the ultimate lifestyle. We have to go the other way, and program into our lives the desire and even the need to generate more energy inside ourselves. Physical fitness is one of the best forms of insurance against civilization disease.

One of the biggest health hazards in a high-energy-use society is overexposure to synthetic chemicals. It's important to understand that the chemical obstacle course through which we must thread our way is made possible only by high energy inputs. If energy and energy-source raw materials like coal, oil, and gas were not so freely available, we would be forced to create for ourselves an environment which is much more natural—and which would bear a closer chemical resemblance to life in under-developed countries.

Nuclear power, which was promised to be the ultimate answer to our needs for external energy, is now seen increasingly as part of a nightmare from which we are slowly awakening. All the assurances of health and safety which were given so freely years ago are now crumbling. The discrediting of the Rasmussen report, which predicted that there would almost never be a reactor accident, is only part of the picture.

What about the toxic wastes that are created by nuclear reactors? There's no way as yet to reprocess them safely, and even if a way to do that is found, how will they be transported safely over the streets, highways, railroads, and rivers to get to the reprocessing plant?

According to Richard G. Piccioni, a postdoctoral fellow at Rockefeller University who wrote recently to the *New York Times*, each year a typical commercial nuclear power reactor produces wastes containing some 130 million curies of radioactivity, "an amount of 10 times that remaining after the detonation of a one-megaton thermonuclear warhead." Dr. Piccioni went on to note that the inhalation of as little as one-millionth of a curie "is virtually certain to cause cancer and genetic damage," and that millions of curies are present in the nuclear wastes "in chemical forms well suited to dispersal into the environment and incorporation into living animals, notably by inhalation."

And the danger that such a dispersal will occur sooner or later during waste transport seems considerable. One physicist serving on a Task Force on the Transport of Radionuclides through Urban Environments has testified before the Department of Transportation that the tests used to affirm the absolute safety of casks for nuclear wastes were inadequate. He also stated that when the containers were subjected to actual test and field conditions, they leaked and suffered dangerous warping of internal steel linings.

The risks of transport aside, there is now evidence that even the small amount of radiation which is released from a normally functioning nuclear plant is not totally without harm. And of great concern are recent observations that these supposedly low levels of radioactivity have a worse effect on people when mixed with the chemical insults that are a normal part of life in developed countries. I am convinced that if honest and unbiased appraisals of nuclear hazards were made, there would be no way to continue that energy technology in the face of the strong public protests that would inevitably result. What new tragedy will it take to wake people up?

Don't let the advocates of nuclear power try to scare you into thinking that the alternative to fission in our future is a return to primitive life. We are so overenergized that we could reduce our energy usage rate by at least 30 percent and still enjoy the benefits of a rich lifestyle. There is now considerable excess generating capacity, and aggressive development of solar power combined with new conservation methods could assure good supplies of energy well into the future.

There is still time for us to make the choices that will lead us to a healthful energy future. And the choice need not be between the life we lead now and a return to living the way our primitive ancestors did. By making intelligent decisions about how we let energy flow into and out of our lives, we can easily create a more healthful environment for ourselves while retaining the truly good aspects of the American way of life.

The Pulse
of Your Life

The rate at which your heart beats will tell you much about how well you personally are using energy. Even more important, if you check your heart rate regularly and try to lower it (within reason), you can achieve important health and fitness benefits.

The purpose of taking your pulse is to find the number of times your heart beats in a minute. The so-called normal pulse is counted when you are at rest, although it is very useful to take your pulse during and after exercise as well.

Here is how to do it. Turn upward the palm of your right hand. Place the tips of the first and second fingers of your left hand across the wrist area of your right hand. The tips of those fingers should touch the hollow spot just to the right of the ligaments that run down the center of your wrist. When you press lightly into that little valley, you should feel the blood pulsating through the radial artery.

I suggested that you feel for the pulse with your left hand, because that's the one on which most people wear their wristwatches. You need a watch with a good second hand, and you should wear it or hold it where you can see it easily.

Most people take their pulse for fifteen seconds, then multiply by four to get the rate of beats per minute. You'll get slightly better accuracy by counting for thirty seconds, or even for a full minute.

What is a normal pulse rate? A better question would be: What range should your pulse be in to signify that you are in good health and have achieved your fitness potential? I reject normality as a reasonable standard for setting health goals. Current sources say you are normal if your pulse rate at rest is anywhere from 50 to 90 beats a minute. What they mean is that if you stand on an average street corner and take the resting pulse rate of everyone passing who is not frankly sick, you'll get rates anywhere between 50 and 90 per minute. But if you look closely at all those whose rates are over 75—for example, if you give them complete fitness tests—you will find that many do not have hearts and lungs of sufficient strength to do a good job of supplying oxygen to the tissues of their bodies.

Fast heart rate at rest is a sign that the heart is too weak. With each pulsation, it moves less blood than it should through the circulatory system. Therefore, it has to work faster, and you might even say harder than it was designed to. The heart of a person with low fitness and a high heart rate could beat fifteen thousand more times a day than the heart of someone who is fit. Over a long period of time, such rapid beating of the heart sets up a chain reaction of detrimental effects.

There are, of course, exceptions to the pulse rate-fitness rules. Abnormal situations can change your pulse rate. And certain illnesses can cause bradycardia (pulse slower than 60 beats per minute) or tachycardia (pulse faster than 100 beats per minute). Use of drugs can also cause tachycardia. (Young children usually have faster pulse rates than adults. So don't worry if your child's pulse is in the upper range of normal.)

Assuming that you are in normal health, there's no mystery to the challenge of strengthening your heart and causing it to beat more slowly. That is done by "working" your heart, causing it to beat more rapidly for short periods. Each time your heart is forced to beat faster by gentle, rhythmic exercise, it becomes a little bit stronger. Even fifteen minutes a day of such exercise, if carried out for a few weeks, will begin to produce a lowering of your heart rate.

Here is how that mechanism of heart improvement works. When you go for a brisk walk, or jog, or swim, or ride a bicycle, the stress on your muscles causes them to need more oxygen. They get that oxygen from arterial blood, but exercise makes your muscles need more, so chemical signals are sent back to the heart asking for help. In response, your heart beats faster, sending more of that precious oxygen.

The process of doing that extra work exercises the heart, causing it to grow stronger and more efficient. Exactly the same thing happens when you exercise your arm muscles by lifting a weight. Your biceps strengthen as a result of doing that work, and soon you are able to lift a weight that is twice as heavy. Do that often enough and you will become very strong. Stress your heart regularly with gentle exercise and it too will become very strong. Because of that strength, it will be able to send more blood and oxygen to your muscles with each beat, thereby saving itself much work. Your heart rate at rest will decline.

How much do you have to exercise to gain that extra heart efficiency? Again, by feeling and counting your pulse, you can gain much valuable information. As you walk, jog, cycle, or swim, stop occasionally and see what your heart is doing. You will notice right away that it is much easier to take your pulse when you have worked up a little sweat and have your body "engine" running faster than a mere idle. Your heart is now pumping hard, and simply by placing your hand on the side of your neck, right under your chin, you can feel the blood coursing through your carotid artery.

Young and vigorous people can get their heart rates up to 150 to 170 beats a minute during hard exercise. Older people should aim for lower rates during exercise. Anything over 100 will probably produce a training effect and benefit your health. The faster you get your heart to beat, though, the more benefit it will receive in a shorter time. Twenty minutes of jogging or cycling that keeps your heart going at 120 beats a minute is probably the equal of an hour and a half of walking that raises your pulse to 100.

Those are rough guesses. I simply want to point out that any gentle, rhythmic exercise is beneficial, but to get the most benefit you must push yourself to the point where your heart gets a workout. Can you exercise so much that your resting pulse rate gets too low? The answer is no. Some athletes, such as professional bicycle racers, have resting pulse rates as low as 35 beats a minute. And they enjoy extremely good heart health.

If you are flabby and out of shape, and if you can convince yourself to keep your pulse rate over 120 beats a minute for half an hour—and do that five days a week for three weeks—you'll probably find that your heart rate at rest has gone down. You will also begin to feel better. Your head will seem more clear, and your outlook on life more hopeful.

Then a fascinating thing will happen. Your body will start talking to you. At first it will happen while you are walking, or cycling, or jogging. You will experience the high feeling of living in a warm body, in which every fiber has been made supple and efficient by the free flow of oxygen, blood, and body fluids. Self-generated warmth is a rare thing, which many people never experience once they pass the early teen years and fall into the slow, dull pace of adulthood. Through the expression of that warmth, your body will tell you that it has been kept bound up by your previous lack of interest in its potential. The faster pulsing of your heart will be matched by new thoughts of expanding horizons in your head.

Later, after you have cooled down, your body will talk to you in a way you may not ever have experienced before. You will feel that communication. Not in words, but in waves of peacefulness. From stronger muscles and organs will come new feelings of confidence and inner control.

But don't be content with experiencing your pulse through exercise. To achieve the greatest possible health and satisfaction, you really should think about and feel more clearly the larger pulses of our physical existence.

Life is not meant to be lived in a flat way. Our evolutionary heritage has formed us to live most efficiently in large pulses. In a true state of health, for example, we achieve a sleep so deep it mimics death. On arising from that sleep, we have a renewed power of life. Were we to try to mix sleep and wakefulness throughout the twenty-four-hour day, we would soon collapse. Our bodies were made to be either awake or asleep, in large pulses of time.

Eating follows the same pattern. If you took all the food you normally eat in a day and nibbled at it continually instead of eating regular meals, your stomach would rebel. Our digestive systems are formed to accept a good bulk of food spaced at four- or five-hour intervals throughout the day, and we benefit also from the ten- to twelve-hour fast at night. When a meal is eaten, all the metabolic processes necessary to digest and use that food energy are put into play. They are stressed—called upon to work for a short time. Then when the job of digestion is finished, they rest again. It is a process similar to stressing the heart during rhythmic exercise: a short period of work, followed by rest and renewed strength. Change that natural pattern of eating in pulses and your system becomes weaker.

One of the most interesting of the large pulses is our built-in defense mechanism against danger, the so-called flight or fight reflex. We have the equipment within us to respond effectively to danger. As soon as we see a great threat coming our way, the adrenaline rushes through our veins, giving us a sudden burst of strength and efficiency. That is not really an unpleasant feeling, especially if the danger is something under control, like a sporting challenge. Many times I've felt the adrenaline flow when I was playing a game and feared losing, when I knew I had the ability to win. The extra push from my adrenal gland was a real help, and the feeling of electric tension was followed by a renewed sense of being alive.

There are other great pulses of life which change over far larger periods of time. Human beings, like other animals, are naturally tuned to live and even eat differently with the changing seasons. In a more natural state, we would change some part of our diet almost every month. Now, with central heating, air-conditioning, and fruits shipped in from the tropics, we tend to live the same kind of lives all year long. That has a flattening effect on our whole experience of life. Almost without realizing it, people have slipped into a way of life which is physically far less exciting than it should be, and is actually unhealthful as a result.

Some of the big pulses have been retained in our modern lifestyle. We still eat and sleep in large pulses. But mechanization has robbed most people of the necessity to raise the pulse rate of their heart, unless they make a conscious effort to go for a walk or do other forms of exercise. At home or at work, we are seldom called upon to do things that get us warmed up inside and cause our heart to pump along at the fast rate needed to keep it healthy. That is a health tragedy and an important cause of much illness.

I hope I haven't made these words about the feeling of your

pulse and the introducing of new cycles into your life sound like something only for younger people. I am not really talking about athletics in the usual sense. Everyone, no matter how old, should still have an interest in the pulse of his or her life and can try to change the pace of living for the better. Studies with very old people have shown that even walking a few steps a day can have a training effect. Walking one hundred feet today makes walking one hundred ten tomorrow easier. What counts is not how strong or willing you are when you start, but making a start and feeling the life force grow in your body as you proceed.

Taking Charge of Your Blood Pressure

ou're lucky—you have a good, low blood pressure. You are going to live a long time."

That wasn't my fortune-teller talking. It was my osteopath, Dr. Chester Kirk. I had come to him to have my upper back muscles manipulated, and as part of his office routine he had measured my blood pressure. The visit took place about twenty-five years ago, but I often think about it. Dr. Kirk was well ahead of his time in realizing that blood pressure measurements of healthy people should be made routinely, and that having a low-normal pressure is one of the best predictors of a long life.

Blood pressure readings are given in two numbers. The first number is the higher, and is called the systolic measurement. It reflects the pressure in your arteries while your heart is in the act of pumping. The second number—the diastolic—is lower and indicates the pressure in the arteries while your heart is resting between beats. Both numbers are important. To be considered normal, your reading should be under 140/90. I feel that a lower pressure, in the region of 120 over 70, is the mark of real health.

People with blood pressure in the low range are better off, because some of their most vital organ systems receive less strain. Higher pressure causes the blood to press harder against the arteries, and also stresses the small vessels in the kidneys and brain. Pressure-strained arteries tend to harden faster. Eventually they grow stiff and less resilient. There can be minor blowouts of vessels in the kidneys. High blood pressure can also cause the bursting of a vessel in the brain—a stroke. The heart itself is eventually weakened by the strain of pushing blood hard through the system for many years.

Everyone should know his or her blood pressure. It is even a good idea to write down your blood pressure readings as they are taken over the years. There is a tendency for blood pressure to increase as you age. That is not healthful or even normal—but it can happen. You don't feel anything. There seldom are symptoms of high blood pressure. But it tends to go up with the passing of years, and you should know if that is happening.

The biggest name in blood pressure research and treatment these days is John H. Laragh, M.D., of the New York Hospital-Cornell Medical Center in New York. He is famous for discovering that essential hypertension, the condition which causes blood pressure to rise gradually, is actually a group of different maladies. Clear insights into the nature of high blood pressure, and the need for different ways to treat it, are provided by Dr. Laragh's research and special treatment programs.

One form of high blood pressure is caused simply by too much blood in the arterial system. Eating salt increases the amount of blood in your body. Some people can't eliminate that extra salt as well as others, and their blood volume increases. That type of hypertension, says Dr. Laragh, can be treated with a low-salt diet and diuretic drugs, which reduce the amount of fluid in the body. It is a less dangerous type of hypertension. A rather complicated series of tests is required to demonstrate that high blood pressure is actually caused by too much blood volume.

Another kind of rise in blood pressure is caused by the presence in the body of too much renin (pronounced ree-nin), a chemical messenger produced in the kidney. Through a rather complicated chain of chemical events, the excess renin causes the blood vessels to constrict—become narrower. That naturally raises the blood pressure.

People with high-renin hypertension have a greater problem on their hands. Proper treatment for their condition is more complicated, and can call for the services of a physician with a clear understanding of blood chemistry and access to good test facilities. These people can also have the "too much blood" kind of hypertension as well as the kind caused by a change in their blood chemistry.

Researchers are now finding that high blood pressure is not limited to adults. At a young age—one to three months—infants with a tendency toward hypertension already show signs of a blood pressure higher than normal, according to R. Curtis Ellison, M.D., co-director of Children's Hospital's hypertension center in Boston.

"Until recently, medical science hasn't really known the average blood pressure range for children," Dr. Ellison says. "However, present findings indicate the average blood pressure for a child five years old is 100/60. This rises throughout the school years and reaches 120/80 by the time a child graduates from high school. These figures represent the upper limits and ideally they should be lower."

Determining which children might develop high blood pressure is an important step in Dr. Ellison's preventive program. He believes family history provides a good predictor of future blood pressure problems. Children whose parents and grandparents have high blood pressure are likely to inherit the tendency and become victims of hypertensive disease as adults.

"Chances of developing high blood pressure will be considerably reduced if the tendency is recognized early and preventive measures are initiated," Dr. Ellison claims. To detect early increases in blood pressure, he recommends that physicians note any family history of hypertension and take blood pressure readings during the annual physical examination of all children three years old and over. He also advises that obesity in children should be avoided, especially during rapid growth periods such as the first year of life and early adolescence, and that salt consumption of infants and children should be restricted. Children should participate in regular exercise programs throughout childhood. Dr. Ellison also points out that the same preventive measures apply to adults.

All of these insights into blood pressure intrigued me, and I decided to make an appointment with Dr. Laragh for the double purpose of getting more information about his methods of diagnosis and treatment, and finding out more about myself. Although I was sure I didn't have treatable hypertension, I thought it would be worthwhile getting checked by the top person in the field.

When I arrived Dr. Laragh was showing around a delegation of Russian physicians. Like the millions of people in America with high blood pressure, doctors too are confused and troubled by hypertension diagnosis and therapy. There is a big need for a better answer to the problem, and many people think Dr. Laragh has it. No wonder he and the thirteen other doctors who work at his hypertension clinic are getting so much attention.

Finally, the Russian delegation went off for a technical briefing, and Dr. Laragh had some time for me. I found him to be a vigorous spokesman for his own ideas—not critical of other methods but very clear in saying that his method is good and should be used more widely. Renin is the key, he feels. Find out if the patient is producing extra renin, as is true of more than half of the people who come to him. Then learn how that renin is reacting with related chemical messengers in the body. After doing that you are on the way to understanding what type of high blood pressure you are dealing with and how to treat it. "The lab that's selling renin test kits tells me they are going fast," he told me.

Finally, we got around to me. I said I had come for an examination as well as an interview. Dr. Laragh had to get back to his Russians, so he called in David B. Case, M.D., at that time clinical director of the hypertension center. He also was busy, but could see me in twenty minutes.

"We'll put your waiting time to good use," Dr. Case said. "Come with me."

He took me to another room in which there was an automatic blood pressure measuring device. I sat next to it in a soft, relaxing chair and Dr. Case wrapped the cuff around my arm.

"Every two minutes this machine will take your blood pressure, and record the figures on a chart. I don't want you to peek and see what's happening. No biofeedback. Just sit and read this copy of *Time* magazine," he ordered.

The machine inflated the cuff for the first reading and Dr. Case looked at the chart.

"Hm . . . 135 over 95. That's a level we would be interested in," he said, and left the room to finish examining his other patient.

For a few seconds I felt bad, because that reading was higher than I wanted it to be. But I soon relaxed and in fact almost dozed off while the robot took more readings—sixteen in all. After about half an hour, Dr. Case came back, unhooked me from the machine, and removed the chart. We walked to his office.

"You're going to be interested in this," he said. "You have a classic case of 'white coat hypertension.' A doctor wearing a white coat takes your blood pressure and your reading is high. When the doctor isn't there, your pressure goes down."

The chart showed clearly that the first measurement of my blood pressure was higher than all the others. With Dr. Case out of the room, the next reading dropped to 125 over 79. Then my pressure fell even lower. Dropping out that first "white coat" reading, all the others averaged out to about 118 over 73—quite good numbers to have.

Other people undoubtedly suffer from similar misreadings of their blood pressure when it is taken just once under circumstances creating anxiety. In fact, "white coat hypertension" could be very widespread. The proper procedure is for a nurse or physician to take several readings, spaced over a period of time, but few do that.

One approach gaining in popularity is for people to take their own blood pressure readings. You are more relaxed by yourself or with your family, and the measurement of blood pressure can then be uninfluenced by the stress of a clinic atmosphere. There are a few problems with self-measurement, though. One is that many of the sphygmomanometers sold for home use need to be checked every once in a while to be sure they're registering accurately. I was advised by Dr. Case to get the kind which measures with a column of mercury. They tend to cost more but don't need to be checked for accuracy. A typical model sells for about forty to fifty dollars.

Although taking blood pressure readings is not terribly complicated, it does take a certain amount of skill plus an interest in accurate measurement. Many people need instruction before they can handle the test effectively.

What should you do if your pressure continuously exceeds 140 over 90? If you are overweight, eat less so that your weight declines. That is important. If you are sedentary, start a program of regular exercise. Walking for an hour or more a day is a good way to start.

Cutting back on the amount of salt you eat could be very important in controlling hypertension. There is still controversy on that point, with some physicians, like Dr. Laragh, taking the position that salt restriction is only important in the control of certain types of high blood pressure. Others feel—as I do—that everyone should eat less salt, to both prevent and treat hypertension.

If those self-help methods don't work, see your doctor. But make sure you go to a good doctor, who has the interest and background to measure your blood pressure accurately and treat it properly. Too many physicians don't know enough about blood pressure diagnosis and treatment to provide the kind of care that is necessary.

Irvine H. Page, M.D., a well-known medical leader, has railed against the low quality of hypertension care in the *Journal of the American Medical Association*. Much hypertension is misdiagnosed, he says. Then, many physicians try to oversimplify treatment, by prescribing a regimen recommended by some drug company and letting their office staff monitor results—which often aren't good. And he feels that the kind of valuable but sophisticated treatment provided by Dr. John H. Laragh and similar hypertension centers is beyond the understanding of most physicians.

The ultimate answer to high blood pressure has not yet been

found. But many people can help themselves enormously by controlling weight, watching salt intake, exercising, and being sure to get an accurate blood pressure measurement. Remember, it is not normal for blood pressure to rise with advancing age. Prevention of the problem should be possible.

Smoke Affects
Your Heart

Although cigarette smoking has not been linked to hypertension directly, it is a major health threat in ways we're just beginning to learn about. Everyone, of course, is aware that substances in tobacco smoke can cause lung cancer and emphysema. Almost as well known is the effect of tobacco smoke on the pipes leading into the lungs—the bronchi. Chronic bronchitis is a problem that many smokers have to contend with.

The effect of smoking on the heart and the circulatory system is much more mysterious. We don't visualize tobacco smoke getting into the heart as easily as we imagine it penetrating the lungs and its tissue. For that reason, the connection between smoking and heart health is not well understood by the average person, nor is heart disease widely accepted as a bad result of the smoking habit. Sure, we all know that smokers are told to stop by their physicians after they show signs of heart trouble or have an attack. But why? What is happening inside the smoker's body that hurts the heart? Few nondoctors can answer that question.

Actually, tobacco smoke hurts the heart more than it does the lungs. That may be hard to believe, but it's true. "The major organ most affected by smoking is the heart," Anthony Owen Colby, M.D., said in an article in *Modern Medicine*. Bar graphs in the American Heart Association's recently published *Heart Book* back up this statement. One graph shows the effect of smoking on the rate of first heart attack among men from thirty to fifty-nine over a ten-year period. Men puffing more than one pack a day experience over three times as many heart attacks as those who have never smoked. Another graph reveals that men from thirty-five to fifty-four who smoke two packs or more a day are ten times more likely to suffer a heart attack than nonsmokers in the general population. According to the U.S. Public Health Service figures cited by Dr. Colby, smokers who do get a heart attack also have a twenty-one-times-greater risk of dying from that attack than a nonsmoking heart attack victim.

It is also known that the act of smoking combines with other bad habits that can lead to heart attack in a way that multiplies the chance of affliction or death. In other words, smoking hurts the heart on its own and in combination with other habits like lack of exercise, tension, wrong eating, and so forth.

OK. There's no doubt that smoking is bad for the heart! But what actually happens to relate a puff on a cigarette to the process of heart weakening?

Carbon monoxide is one villain in the drama. Tobacco smoke contains that odorless gas, which has a unique power to hurt the heart. Oxygen, not carbon monoxide, is the gas that the heart loves. "The heart utilizes more oxygen than any other organ in the body," Dr. Colby points out. And he says further that the heart takes from the blood 100 percent of the oxygen that is delivered to it, even during sleep and other periods of rest.

When carbon monoxide enters the lungs, the mechanism of oxygen delivery to the heart is disrupted in a drastic way. Hemoglobin, the blood substance that picks up oxygen in the lungs and delivers it to the heart, goes berserk in a peculiar way. Hemoglobin, perversely, prefers carbon monoxide to oxygen—in fact, prefers it 250 times as much. So levels above 5 percent of carbon monoxide in the air drastically reduce the amount of oxygen that the heart is able to get. When that happens, the heart is not able to function with its normal efficiency, and has to beat faster to avoid oxygen starvation.

Not only that. The carbon monoxide in cigarette smoke can cause a rare disease of the blood itself, which was given the name "smoker's polycythemia" in an article in the *New England Jour-*

nal of Medicine by J. Robert Smith, M.D., and Stephen A. Landaw, M.D., Ph.D.

The word polycythemia describes a condition in which the blood has more than normal amounts of red blood cells and also hemoglobin. Putting carbon monoxide into the air breathed by the lungs not only keeps oxygen from getting to the heart in sufficient amounts, but also signals the body to create more red cells and hemoglobin to feed that vital gas to the heart. The result is that the heart gets so thick with red cells that the flow of blood is reduced. The inability of the blood to carry oxygen to the brain causes sluggishness, irritability, headache, and dizziness. Sometimes people with polycythemia faint, or stop having normal feeling in their hands and feet. There is also what my medical dictionary describes as "a feeling of fullness in the head." The skin may turn blue, and the smaller veins become more prominent. In some cases, the tips of the fingers become enlarged because blood simply can't flow out of them in the normal way.

Did you think that doctors stopped bleeding people back in the early 1800s? Well, think again! A standard treatment for mild cases of polycythemia is to bleed the patient—to get rid of some of the excess red cells.

Returning to carbon monoxide, doctors know that it not only cuts off flow of oxygen to the heart, but on its own harms cells which are vital to the heart's proper functioning. Carbon monoxide causes the mitochondria (the power plants of the cell) to swell and disintegrate. The injured cells are not able to produce energy—and therefore weaken the heart.

Again, that's not all. Dramatic research recently reported by Poul Astrup of Copenhagen shows that carbon monoxide has yet another effect on the heart. Blood containing carbon monoxide, he found, prevents cells that make up the lining of the coronary arteries from exchanging oxygen and other nutrients with each other—a vital process since these cells (almost unique among all body cells) have no other way to get nourishment. The result is degeneration of the interior of the coronary arteries of a type very similar to atherosclerosis.

So much for carbon monoxide. The nicotine in tobacco smoke also has a bad effect on the heart. Nicotine is a powerful drug, and it is particularly harmful to a weakened heart because it upsets the normal electrical impulses which are the sparks that cause the heart to function. The importance of electricity to the heart becomes apparent when you remember that the electro-cardiogram, which is a way of examining the heart's electrical profile, is the basic tool for assessing heart health. A nicotine-influenced heart doesn't get its electrical signals quite straight. One part of the heart tends to beat ahead of its normal time, and another tries to beat behind schedule. Not being able to beat with the proper synchronization, the nicotined heart tends (under stress) to relapse into the very fast, uncontrolled ventricular beats which render the heart useless for pumping blood. "In reality," says Dr. Colby, "it is precisely this mechanism that leads to sudden death."

We need to separate what is new and what is old about the relationship of smoking to heart and circulatory problems. Quite old indeed is the knowledge that smoking reduces circulation of the blood and is generally bad for heart health. I remember as a child (about forty years ago) being told the sad tale of a cigarette-smoking relative who got Buerger's disease—which caused some of that person's toes to need amputation. Also, at least ten years ago I saw a demonstration by a physical educator of the immediate effect of smoking one cigarette on heart rate. A simple apparatus attached to a smoker's finger showed that the pulse increased and skin temperature decreased after a few puffs.

The new information about the smoking-heart relationship is opening our eyes to exactly what is going on in the body when tobacco smoke (either smoked or inhaled passively) replaces pure air in the lungs. We now know, for example, that carbon mon-oxide is as bad a factor in tobacco smoke as is nicotine—if not worse—and we can explain clearly to people the many ways that smoking is known to have a detrimental effect on health and vigor. The mystery of smoking's effect has been replaced by clear, scientifically proven knowledge. (And keep in mind that we're talking only about the smoking-heart connection. I could give you similar information about smoking's effect on allergies, mus-cle tone, physical appearance, resistance to colds, speed of wound healing, sex drive, and even the sense of taste and smell.)

Most exciting of all is the way this new understanding of the effect of smoking on heart health and blood circulation points toward an effective cure for the smoking habit itself. The heart is tremendously receptive to help that we can give it by changing our lifestyle. By avoiding smoking, eating wisely, exercising sensibly, and using nutritional supplements, we can often build heart and circulatory health at middle and even old age to a point far above that important organ's efficiency during an earlier age.

What we are finding is that the very methods that are known to improve heart health also help build the needed motivation to stop smoking. Exercise is but one example. Regular, rhythmic physical activity strengthens the heart and also does something inside a person that reduces the urge to smoke. Samuel Fox, M.D., former head of the American Heart Association's Exercise Committee, says that "rare is the vigorous exerciser who will continue to smoke." Ronald M. Lawrence, M.D., president and founder of the American Medical Jogger's Association, echoes that view. "When people start jogging," he says, "they find that smoking impedes their performance and also that cigarettes no longer taste good." So they stop the habit. Smoking is definitely on the decline among people who jog.

A healthful diet emphasizing raw, whole plant foods like seeds, nuts, vegetables, and certain mildly sweet fruits can create the same antismoking effect, according to John Douglass, M.D., of the Southern California Permanente Medical Group.

These ideas and methods give us exactly what is needed to fight the smoking habit, which is without any redeeming social value. We need to show people how they can do things that will help them to feel better and at the same time build the inner motivation to want to live a better life as a nonsmoker. That positive approach—which we now know does work—is far more effective in the long run than warnings about health disaster unaccompanied by suggestions that smokers form new habits which build a reservoir of feel-good sensations.

Yes, smoking will give you cancer. But not smoking will do far more than just help prevent that disease. Combining a healthful diet and regular exercise with the inhaling of smokeless air will lead people to the achievement of a glow of aliveness that is so good it can't be described in words alone. You have to feel it to believe what can happen to you.

Life's Toughest Fight

common misconception is that old people die of disease. They don't. They die of homeostatic failure. The body loses its inner balance, its ability to snap back from the impact of stress. The regulating devices of the body rust and are overwhelmed by the task of trying to keep aged organs and weakened muscles functioning as a balanced unit.

If you disagree, recall gerontologist Alex Comfort's judgment, cited earlier, that cures for cancer and heart failure would add less than three years to the life span of someone over sixty-five. Why is that true? Simply because most people in the sixty-five-or-over class are flirting with homeostatic failure. They are vulnerable to a large number of diseases because their recovery powers are no longer strong. The average person who dies between sixty-five and seventy is found on autopsy to have 5.71 different diseases or "lesions," as the doctors say. Cure two of those, and there are still 3.71 left. I don't say this to be gloomy or pessimistic but to alert you to the facts and to try to make you receptive to a course of action which can help you live for a long time past the "average" age and feel better while doing it.

There is no real escape from growing old. On the other hand, there is no requirement that you have to die when your friends and contemporaries do or that the post-retirement years must be just a waiting period while final decline sets in. The inevitable can be delayed. The fountain of youth may yet be found for those who are willing to stretch life like a rubber band and not try to turn it into an endless conveyor belt.

Before telling you how to stretch life, let me explain homeostasis and aging's effects on it. Homeostasis, according to the Random House dictionary, is "the tendency of a system to maintain internal stability, owing to the coordinated response of its parts to any situation or stimulus tending to disturb its normal condition or function." Homeostasis is the balancing force which tends to compensate and defend the body against any stress.

Consider a young person, in good health and physical condition. At rest his heart may beat only 60 times a minute or as many as 75 times a minute. As he starts to run, however, his body is stressed and more oxygen is needed by his muscles. So the heart beats faster, delivering more fresh, aerated blood and satisfying the muscles' demands. When the heart is beating fast the body is in homeostasis, because the extra oxygen needed can be delivered. The body automatically adjusts the functions of its organs to meet demands on them.

Now let's consider what happens in the body of an older person who perhaps has a touch of emphysema, high blood pressure, excess fat, and poor muscle tone. At rest his body is in homeostasis, but his heart has to beat faster to keep blood circulating and oxygen traveling to the muscles. Consequently, his resting heart rate may be as high as 90 beats a minute. When this older person walks or climbs stairs or tries to shovel snow, there is a real homeostatic crisis. The heart does beat faster; it may go way up to the absolute maximum. The breathing rate increases also, to the point where the person feels "out of breath." Yes, homeostasis is maintained by the extreme efforts of the organs, but eventually a price is paid. The older person is uncomfortable during stress because the homeostatic mechanism can't compensate adequately. Internally, the organs aren't comfortable either. You can say with complete truth then that the body is beginning to break down. Homeostatic failure may not be a disease, but it is the weakness which makes the entry of disease into the body too easy. "Heart attack" may be listed as the cause of death when an elderly man shovels snow and drops dead, but he really died of homeostatic failure. His body simply couldn't adjust to the added stress.

To win this toughest of all challenges and maintain homeostasis for many years, we are going to have to use our heads. The man who shoveled snow and dropped over suffered a failure of homeostasis because he didn't think. He didn't realize that his body was like a giant 747 with the control mechanism of a DC-3, yet he was still trying to fly.

Scientists now know we should concentrate not on finding ways to prolong life when homeostasis is beginning to falter, but on learning how to extend the prime of life by slowing down the biological clock that ticks within. The exact process by which animals and people grow old is still a mystery. But we have made the significant discovery that efforts to slow down aging must start when the organism is young. In fact, the younger the better, for in infancy the body ages faster than at any other time.

That breakthrough was made back in the 1930s, and is now leading to serious discussions about practical ways to extend the human life span. More than forty years ago the late Clive M. McCay, who was professor of animal nutrition at Cornell University, found that the aging process in rats could be slowed by giving them a special diet. He did that by underfeeding rats very early in life, usually just after they were weaned. The animals were given more than adequate amounts of protein, minerals, and vitamins, but few carbohydrates and calories. That diet was maintained until the rats reached maturity.

The McCay diet kept the animals smaller than normal, and also caused some to have impaired development and erratic behavior. In exchange for those losses, however, the rats received the blessing of extremely long life. Some survived for as long as 1,400 days, which in human terms translates into a life span of 140 years. That was a fantastic change in the aging process, an effect that had never been demonstrated before.

Other scientists have recently published reports which add weight to that evidence. Gabriel Fernandes, Associate, and Robert A. Good, Ph.D., M.D., at Memorial Sloan-Kettering Cancer Center in New York, and Edmond Yunis, M.D., professor of pathology at Harvard Medical School, were able to extend the lives of a special strain of mice by giving them an adequate but low-calorie diet. Their mice had a genetic defect which made them susceptible to disease. Eating less delayed the impact of that defect.

Another study showed that rats with a genetic tendency toward fatness lived longer when kept on a low-calorie diet. The late Simon Koletsky, M.D., formerly a professor of pathology at Case Western Reserve Medical School in Cleveland, reported that result in 1976. His low-caloried rats showed resistance to atherosclerosis, and lived longer as a result.

Going beyond animal studies, there's plenty of other evidence that a diet low in calories makes people healthy (as long as you get abundant vitamins and minerals and adequate amounts of protein). In fact, the nutrition literature is full of research reports showing that thin people have special health benefits. True, most of those reports relate to prevention of diseases and conditions like high blood pressure, heart disease, cancer, and diabetes. But it seems logical to me that if a low-calorie diet can help prevent or even cure some of those problems, it is working some magic with the aging process as well.

Convincing circumstantial evidence exists showing that undereating extends life. As a group the people of Abkhasia (in the Soviet Union), Hunza (in Kashmir), and Vilcabamba (in Ecuador) tend to reach great ages, working and playing hard well into their eighties, nineties, and even beyond. Researchers studying these vigorous folks have found that they eat food that is low in calories and fat, though rich in nutrients. Apparently such people achieve superior homeostasis by bringing their energy intake and output into a near-perfect balance.

Actually, no matter how old you are, there is probably still time for you to make homeostasis easier for your body. Becoming lighter if you are overweight helps. Also, the McCay effect can work its magic during maturity as well as in youth. Speaking before a Swiss medical group back in 1953, McCay remarked that "Even starting in middle life, the rats obliged to keep thin had the greater length of life."

Could the same be true for people? I think so. In fact, I think you can do something which may seem quite remarkable, but is really very logical. You can reverse the aging process by losing weight and improving your physical condition. While your years of age will remain the same, you can actually feel younger and regain some of the spark of youthful activity by taking off unneeded pounds.

Think for a moment of what it means to carry around ten or twenty pounds of unneeded weight. When you're young maybe you can handle that, but most Americans get heavier as they age, and are less able to handle that weight without feeling loggy and "old." Try carrying ten pounds around in your hands, or even strapped to your back. You'll soon see how it can drag you down.

So just by lightening your personal burden, losing weight can help you get through the day with new vigor. Your heart and lungs will have less work to do, too, as will other important organs. And if weight loss is combined with exercise to build strength, the return of youthful vigor will be even more remarkable.

Dr. McCay was well aware of the practical implications of his antiaging discovery. He knew that dieting doesn't come easy, even if the prospect of living many added years is at the end of the diet rainbow.

"Foods are needed to bolster the will in persons whose brains cannot control the appetite," he said in one of his articles. "Drinking a suspension of dried brewer's yeast in water just before meals is useful in the attack upon the problem. This high-protein, high-vitamin food has considerable satiety value."

A second route to youthful old age is to train and condition your homeostatic mechanism itself. You can do that easily, no matter what your age, by a routine of regular, moderate, controlled stress. There is a common word for that stress which everyone will understand. Exercise! Yes, bodily movement is a constructive type of stress, and if that stress is moderate and regular, your body will gradually become stronger and will soon be able to accept extra burdens with little strain. You thus reverse a decline toward homeostatic failure. Exercise is the one form of stress which causes the body homeostasis mechanism to be strengthened. It is not harmful if done sensibly.

The ability of the human body to respond to physical conditioning is truly astounding, and the effect remains until well into the so-called aged years. Unless used, muscles atrophy. Unfortunately, as we get older, we tend to think that the days of youthful gamboling are past. Most people over thirty think that it's undignified to run or to ride a bicycle and that walking is a sign that you can't afford a car. They don't realize their bodies still have the power to regain many of the physical powers of youth, if they are cultivated intelligently.

The rejuvenating power of exercise has been demonstrated many times. In one study done for the federal government's Administration on Aging, a group of seventy-year-old men who participated in an exercise program for a year were found to have the physical reactions of forty-year-olds. Others who have gotten the message that exercise can roll back the biological clock are the many 60- to 102-year-old people participating in Preventicare.

In West Virginia there are over two hundred groups in that state-sponsored fitness program. Their members get together for three one-hour sessions every week to tone up their circulation and their muscles. And get a little younger.

Yes, chronological age is not your true age. Every person is different, and no two people born on the same day are really the same age by the time they get past the middle years. Experts on aging are developing a whole new calendar of human life, based not on days or months or years but on analysis of the factors which contribute to homeostasis. Before too long, you will be able to go to a laboratory and take a series of tests that will measure not your degree of sickness, but the power of your body to regulate itself. From that information a prediction could be made as to how far you have traveled along a normal life span.

Imagine the implications of such a breakthrough! Retirement will no longer have to be based on how many times the sun travels across the heavens, but rather on what a man is able to do. A man or woman of seventy-five chronological years may still be actively engaged in guiding human affairs while a "young" fellow of forty winters is put out to pasture because physical tests show that he is close to homeostatic failure. Best of all, people will realize clearly the tyranny of the celestial calendar and will perceive that length of life is something that man himself can control, within certain limits.

The Target
Is Wholeness

Too many health-oriented people are content to accept limits on their well-being. They use one or two health improvement methods, then stop trying to expand their horizons. Eating less to control your weight, for example, is an important health technique. Many people are on diets, and some actually succeed. But not enough dieters go beyond the idea of losing weight and try to improve the quality of the food they eat or try to improve their physical fitness through exercise. If people tried more avenues to health, they would find the goal easier to reach. There is a remarkable interlocking effect among good health practices—each complementing the others, all working together to make our bodies stronger, more vigorous, and more able to resist disease.

How do people get themselves into this narrow corner? I think they are still too sold on the idea of curing disease with one drug, one operation, one diet, or one special technique. When the average person has an ache or pain, he believes one pill will cure him. The truth is that the drugs people take have far less effect than they think. Our bodies eventually heal themselves by drawing on the variety of reserves and curative powers that we possess. Diseases are often caused by a variety of factors and are cured in a variety of ways—not by one particular drug.

A person's view of cure reflects his view of health. Most people become health-minded by getting sick. They get a disease, start worrying, and decide that now is the time to start doing something to really improve their health. Since the idea that disease can be cured in one way is so firmly implanted in the average person's mind, it is little wonder that most people embark on a health-building campaign using only one or two techniques.

Another reason for such narrow approaches is that many leaders in the health field play only one instrument. Old Dr.

Fletcher convinced millions of people to chew their food thoroughly to improve their health. Fletcherism became a household word because the single concept of chewing food was something people could latch on to. When Dr. Fletcher took the podium at his lectures, he preached one sermon, yet made many converts.

Thousands of health-minded people have been indoctrinated over the years by lecturers, but speaking briefly before an audience, no one has the time to convince people of the merits of a variety of health techniques. Most of the ideas that lecturers propound are good, but they each tell of only one and there are so many.

How do we change ourselves? How can we make better use of the many health ideas? First, we must always be willing to examine ourselves critically, keeping our minds open to the possibility that just maybe we aren't always right and that maybe we can find better ways to live. Health-minded people generally consider themselves to be more enlightened than the average person, who allows his body and spirit to be wronged by everyone from doctors to food merchants. We think that in comparison to the man-in-the-street we are aware, open-minded, adventurous, intelligent, and perhaps even attractive. In truth, we probably have only a touch of these good qualities, but have allowed it to inflate our egos. One of the hardest things to do is to look at yourself critically, but that is what we must do to keep climbing to higher levels of health.

We should also keep in mind the real meaning of the word *health*. Health derives from the Anglo-Saxon word *hale*, meaning "whole." Thinking of health as wholeness is far better than the common way of thinking of health as "wellness" or mere absence of symptoms. The word has been so abused, misinterpreted, warped, and corrupted that it may be beyond salvation, and we might benefit more from seeing a new term for the better kind of life that we are trying to build for ourselves. We could do far worse than to aim for wholeness—in body, spirit, and relations with our fellow human beings.

The medical people are largely at fault for the declining status of the word *health*. Historically, doctors have focused their efforts and their expertise on sickness, symptoms, and disease.

In school they spend endless hours poring over pictures and specimens of malignancy, degeneration, weakness, and debilitation. During their working lives doctors fine-tune their senses to the recognition of disease—finding satisfaction when they uncover a unique illness. The result is that the healthy person draws a blank from the average doctor. The surprised physician is in strange country and hardly knows what to say, except to invite the healthy one back in six months in the hope of finding something familiar then.

Yet, to their familiarity with human failure doctors apply the word *health*. They call themselves health workers, and support a variety of health plans, few of which do anything except finance the patching of decay and degeneration usually too far entrenched inside the patient to be reached by the medical techniques now in use.

But let's get back to ourselves. Let's take a critical look. Wholeness should be our goal. *Whole* is a universal word, implying there is more to living longer and feeling better than just following our own pet plans and methods.

One good health practice generally makes others easier. Research has shown that people who exercise regularly can give up cigarettes more easily than people who remain sedentary. And very often cutting back on nicotine, caffeine, sugar, or alcohol will make it easier to get away from other substances on the list. Why? Because all these things create a biochemical imbalance that encourages physiological or psychological dependence. And because their effects on blood and brain chemistry are similar enough so we can readily substitute one addiction for another. Heavy drinkers, for example, often become compulsive sweet-eaters after giving up alcohol. They are just substituting one highly refined kind of carbohydrate for another.

Too often, though, people seem to think that a full load of self-improvement is too difficult to carry. If they find it difficult to diet, they think it will be twice as hard to both diet and walk an hour a day. The truth is, two acts are easier than one. One complements the other, both physically and mentally. When you exercise, your body consumes some of the calories that you eat, without causing you to want to eat extra food. The exercise refreshes your spirit, gives you occasion to reflect on what your body can do, and renews your desire for self-improvement. It is only common sense, after all, that if you are going to diet successfully you are better off being out of the house and moving around than sitting in the kitchen or watching TV.

One of the big barriers to achievement of a whole program of self-improvement is the natural human affinity for the easy way. People tend to skim the scum off the surface of life without getting in deep and really cleaning out the muck. This shallowness is what has led the medical establishment (and the nation's sick people) to the brink of bankruptcy, and all too often people take the same approach to thinking about themselves. They believe real quality of life is an easy chair and several cans of beer every evening.

The human body does not thrive on ease, however. A whole environment is not a place where everything is done for you. The finest view is seen and appreciated only by he who climbs the mountain. Van R. Potter, in *Environmental Research* magazine, suggested that the best environment is one that delivers "optimum stress." The body is always adapting to conditions it faces, Potter pointed out. It is wrong to think that these adaptations are always to unfavorable or bad conditions. Sometimes the stress is really a blessing in disguise, preventing a slide into weakness and eventual illness. One of Potter's most interesting examples involved a subject that has been very much part and parcel of the natural health movement over the centuries—fasting. Not eating from time to time may be just the kind of stress that is good for our health, because when our stomachs become empty the body puts into play certain regulatory mechanisms to balance the system. If we snack all the time, that regulatory plumbing "rusts" from disuse, and our bodies lose some of the wholeness which I believe is essential to real well-being.

Fasting may have been something which you—like me—thought was not beneficial to health, but now, having opened my mind, I can see there is some logic to the concept. It just could be, too, that fasting is an important aid to confidence-building. If you know you can go without food for a day or even for a few meals, you gain greater respect for your body's ability to function under adverse conditions.

One final, important point. We live in a rapidly changing world, and much of that change is in the direction of fragmentation, division, separation, and isolation. Things are coming apart. Why? I think primarily it's the tremendous penetration that unguided science has made into our lives and into our society. People once universally looked to religion as a source of insight into the natural world. Today, religion is relegated to spiritual concerns, and science is expected to tell us how and why the world works. We have been sold the idea that if science seeks the truth about the natural world, its findings will certainly be applied to the benefit of mankind. We are finding two things instead.

First, to investigate the natural world thoroughly, scientists have had to specialize. The scientific body of knowledge about the world is too vast to be grasped by one man or even by one hundred men. So there is less wholeness to our understanding of the world as this specialization of study escalates.

Secondly, the scientific information from the specialties is merged into a technology used to make products and to create services that people often don't really need. The result is the use of perfumed air freshener in a spray can instead of opening the bathroom window. People are sold imitation, synthetic foods with no wholeness. Technology is one of the few unified forces at work on our society, and it is terribly efficient. Moreover, it is not being countered with a whole understanding of what is really good for people.

I believe that our salvation is in our own hands. The people who believe in natural health, completely or in part, are closest to understanding the absolute necessity of wholeness in our lives. We must show even more wholeness in our actions. Let's eat more whole food. Let's use all the systems in our body together, so that we become stronger. Let's show others that we can get more satisfaction by whole, sensible living.

4 WHAT KIND OF PROGRESS DO WE WANT?

A State of Mind

Where does all the dirt come from that is fouling our rivers, our air, our soil, our food, and even the oceans?

We produce it with our thoughts, our overweening ambitions, our desire to live a life of ease and superiority over all other living creatures. Pollution is a state of our minds. We think that the universe revolves around us, that our needs are more important than the needs of all other forms of life. How wrong we are!

Look at each dirty part of this world and you will see—through the murk—a failure of human thinking. Men think they can pack millions of people into New York City and its environs and still dispose of all the sewage and garbage safely. That's not optimism—it's bad thinking. Why should we think we can zoom around the country and into every part of every city with three-hundred-horsepower horseless carriages and not spread manure of some sort? It can't be done, but we think it can.

How could it be possible to generate vast amounts of nuclear power without creating by-products that have a destructive power just as awesome? As Three Mile Island made plain, it isn't possible. But we still think it is.

And farmers and chemical companies still believe they can use powerful poisons to keep damaging insects away from our farms without poisoning us or our insect, bird, and animal friends. Again, that's bad thinking. Many of the chemicals and other eventual pollutants now plaguing us simply aren't necessary for a happy, healthful, satisfying life. Yet we think we need them. That's where we are making our big mistake.

Are you confused by pollution? Do you wonder what really can be done to return our natural environment to the quality we took for granted several decades ago? Well, you probably aren't nearly as confused as some scientists and technologists. They have spent their entire careers believing they could build "better things for better living through chemistry," to borrow just one phrase from the large bank of technological patriotism which keeps our laboratories humming. Now these white-coated men and women are beginning to see many of their advances boomerang, slapping back with ever-increasing force. Just as the medical people have found out that every "wonder drug" has a side effect that can be worse than the disease it cures, so do the miracle washday products foul our rivers, and the convenience foods cause hardening of the arteries and vitamin deficiencies.

Scientists are further confused because they are so fragmented and isolated by the specialization of their training. Chemists tend to know nothing of biology, psychology, or meteorology. Biologists know too little about agriculture, technology, or economics.

Having learned more and more about less and less, they don't know how to think in universal terms. We have not thought it necessary to train people to understand the general problem of living sanely, in tune with our environment. As a result, our intellectual leaders don't understand the human consequences of the technological devices that have become such a big part of our lives.

Technology, wrongly applied with our permission, has fed on our confusion and greed. Unguided, it has bridged the specialization of science and created tools of immense power. Members of each branch of science throw their nuggets of knowledge into the collection plate of the industrial establishment and—with misguided good grace—do not observe the counting process in the back room. They do not supervise the forgers of our industrial society, who merge that knowledge and use it to create things that people think they need.

Horrible thought! Technology is now doing our thinking for us. What is possible to do (technologically) will be done. We are almost blindly devoted to finding the one best way to do every conceivable task, and technology offers such attractive ways to do everything that we can't think of alternatives.

Pollution is the payoff for our bad thinking. As Buckminster Fuller says, every American is now using power equivalent to the work of five hundred human slaves. Even mechanical slaves must be fed. And they produce waste. In America, our mechanical slaves are doing the work of at least 125 billion people. No wonder our environment is becoming degraded and polluted. Any simplistic solution—any technological trick—we use to make that waste less noticeable or less threatening is bound to fail in the long run, although it may provide short-term relief.

Instead of blindly insisting on our "right" to keep using power in self-indulgent ways, we should be trying to design the kind of world we really want. That is our challenge. We have the capability to build almost any kind of future we want, if we apply that strength in the right ways. We may have to learn moderation, using fewer than five hundred slaves apiece though we have the means to harness that many. I think if people learn how to take a clear look at the environment, they will see that a more conservative pace of living can be much more enjoyable than the hectic, impersonal, mechanical routines we now follow.

There's a growing view among perceptive environment-watchers that we are simply applying too much force to a world that is more fragile than we realize. It is time to ease back on the throttle and to move gently into a less high-powered lifestyle. One that is organized around a technology more appropriate to a world rapidly becoming pollution-rich and resource-poor.

Using Leverage to Make Life Easier

The gear system that maximizes the energy put into pedaling a bike has its parallel in many other techniques of energy-wise living. I like to think of such practices as bringing leverage to bear.

Using a lever is the simplest way to do more work with less effort. Suppose you want to move a heavy rock. Lifting it with your hands is out of the question. So you find another smaller rock to use as a fulcrum, and wedge a pole or rod between that pivot point and the rock to be moved. Then only a moderate pressure downward on the lever will lift the rock.

Leverage is a useful principle to know about, but how often do we have to move a heavy rock? And how often do we have a fulcrum and a lever to use when confronted with that task? Most people these days would call for a front-end loader before even thinking about using a lever.

Which is exactly my point. Times have changed, and simple methods of doing work very efficiently are being overlooked. Even our mental outlook toward physical work has changed, with less emphasis now being placed on learning how to use the leverage in our own bodies.

I often think back about the time I was taught to use a scythe by an old master of that beautiful and efficient tool. My first efforts to cut weeds were ridiculously awkward. I could raise the scythe a yard or so above the ground, then bring the blade crashing down on the tall weeds broadside. Very little work got done, my hands blistered, and within ten minutes I was exhausted.

"Here, let me show you how to do that," the old master said. "Stand straight and relaxed, like this," he demonstrated. "Don't swing the thing wildly, but pivot around the center of your body. Slide the blade in on those weeds from the side, and slice into them at an angle. That way you keep plenty of momentum in your blade, without using so much effort."

When I used his time-honored method—which is the right way to scythe—the work became easier. That long blade began to slide through weeds cleanly, with its own weight helping to do the work. Sure it took me a few days to build up my shoulder and arm muscles, but within a week I could keep that scythe going for hours at a time without tiring.

Scything properly is a good demonstration of the principle of leverage. The wooden handle of the scythe is the lever, and you, its operator, are the fulcrum point. In this case, the muscle power comes right at the hinge point instead of at the end of the lever, but the basic principle remains the same.

The scythe is rarely used today. It is considered obsolete. That is unfortunate, because countless American young men are not learning the feel of their own bodies as fulcrums for a grass-cutting lever. Tractors and power mowers are great grass-cutting tools, but their efficiency stems from a different source—the internal combustion engine. We need those engines and the remarkable tools they power, but I think we should also keep alive the old knowledge of the efficient use of simple tools.

Even more valuable would be to expand our appreciation of the advantage of leverage into other areas. The people of China do this with great effect, for they have had to live with so little for so many centuries that they have incorporated leverage into many aspects of their home life. It is not exactly leverage in the classic sense of physics, but efficiency that is so clever and useful that leverage is the only word to use to describe it.

Consider the way the Chinese cook food, for example. Their basic utensil is the wok, a round-bottomed pan that makes the most efficient use possible of a small fire. Heat from the fire curls upward around the wok, warming all parts of the pot. The wok has no useless sides—every part of it is used for cooking.

But wait, there is more to say about the leverage of a Chinese cooking fire. In northern China the heat of the fires is not sent up the chimney to be wasted. It is diverted through the *kang* (pronounced like gong, but with a *k* in front), which is a bed for sleeping and resting made of clay. The draft of the cooking fire is diverted through a maze of pipes inside the kang before being sent up a chimney. So that bed of clay is warmed by heat that would otherwise be wasted.

The Chinese also make use of nutritional leverage. The simple act of multiplying food value by sprouting is leverage in the best sense of the word. Even the way food is eaten can provide nutritional leverage. Consider the problem of getting enough protein. The Chinese found a long time ago that if they ate rice at one meal and bean curd made from soybeans at another, they tended not to feel well. They knew nothing about protein, but they knew when their food wasn't helping them enough. So they began eating bean curd and rice together, which gave them protein of excellent quality. William Shurtleff and Akiko Aoyagi give some figures on that effect in their excellent *Book of Tofu*.

"By serving only 3½ ounces of tofu (bean curd) together with 1¼ cups of brown rice," they say, "we obtain 32 percent more protein than if we served those foods separately."

Fortunately, some Americans are today using that kind of nutritional leverage, but there is still room for improvement. The typical way is to rely on meat as the basic protein source, which is an unleveraged approach to the protein challenge. You can get your protein that way, but you also get too much animal fat, which means excess calories. Using cereals, beans, and other plant foods as basic protein can produce a healthier diet that is lower in calories, but rich in needed nutrients.

Gardeners have to use a different kind of leverage to be able to till the soil of a small plot with the small amount of horsepower (or people power) available to them. A farmer can bull his way into a field with a tractor of a hundred or more horsepower, pulling five plows or other equipment weighing several tons. But the gardener has to use subtler tactics.

Mulching and composting are excellent examples of garden leverage. Adding some organic matter to the soil makes it soft and crumbly within just a few seasons, so tillage can be accomplished with much less effort. The late Ruth Stout's thick-mulch system is a fine example of garden leverage. After a few years of heavy mulching, such soil gets so soft and workable that it doesn't have to be tilled at all. A gardener using this approach merely moves aside the mulch, places the seed on the soil, stirs the mulch back over it, and waits for harvest time.

For actually digging into the soil, the rotary tiller is the best example of the application of leverage. Pulling a moldboard plow with a garden tractor of only a few horsepower is a difficult challenge, unless your soil is extremely soft. But a rotary tiller applies that light horsepower to the task of tillage in a much more clever way. Those rotating tines nibble away at a heavy soil in small bites, instead of trying to dig right in and lift the whole top layer of soil over at one time. And the shaft around which the tines rotate is geared way down, so that the actual power behind each of those small "plows" is magnified enormously. With a tiller, a gardener can open soil as efficiently as a farmer can break the clods of a large field. The area tilled is smaller, of course, but the nature of the work is the same.

There are also biological ways to use leverage in the soil. Growing legume green-manure crops that are properly inoculated with commercial cultures of root-zone bacteria is a fine example. Other types of bacteria, such as the free-living, nitrogen-capturing *Azotobacter* also can do large amounts of work in the garden without costing much or requiring hard work by the gardener.

The only problem with *Azotobacter* is that they stop collecting nitrogen from the air as soon as they get enough to meet their own needs. So scientists are at work seeking new types of those bacteria that are more efficient. It is hoped that they eventually can find *Azotobacter* which will keep on sucking in the nitrogen far beyond their own needs, thereby supplying plenty of that element for hungry farm and garden plants. Some progress has already been made, and superior types of *Azotobacter* cultures are now being sold.

Other bacteria are able to release phosphorus that is locked up in the soil. They are called phosphobacterin and have been used widely as natural "fertilizers" in Poland and Russia. Do they really work? Can they "lever" more phosphorus out of the soil, cutting the need for fertilizer? Scientists in Poland claim excellent results, and research is being carried out elsewhere to see if phosphobacterin can become another useful garden tool.

I could go on citing many other examples of areas of work, transportation, and conservation where the principle of leverage could be used more vigorously. In almost every aspect of life, it is possible to look at our liberal use of energy to power engines, motors, and tools of all kinds and see waste, because the idea of leverage has been forgotten, or downgraded. It is time to change that.

The Leisure Fiasco

There is an innate satisfaction—and yes, pleasure—in using leverage to achieve something worthwhile. Compare that for a minute with the emptiness of spare time spent conspicuously consuming goods and other forms of energy.

Leisure! What a pain it is for most people. We have the free hours. We have the money to travel and to buy leisure-time equipment. We even have a strong inclination to make the best possible use of our spare time. Yet we fail miserably and utterly. Our nonwork time is often spent in frantic pursuit of an ever-receding goal of personal fulfillment. We rush hither and yon to pack the most enjoyment into our weekends and vacations, then stagger back to our offices and factories to recover from the drain made on our bodies and minds. Plainly, we aren't leisurely about our leisure. What is wrong?

Swedish economist Staffan B. Linder says our big trouble is that we expect money to buy enjoyable leisure, when the reverse is true. In his view we are barred from full enjoyment of our free time by the very goods and gadgets we buy to amuse ourselves. A sailboat looks like fun when seen at a dealer's dock, but when we own one the chores of management tend to overpower the fun potential. The same is true of many smaller items. We surround ourselves with stereo equipment, records, video tapes and games, sporting equipment, cameras, and other goods for amplifying our leisure, then get mildly frantic because we don't have the time to use them. Hours that should be spent in constructive leisure are often devoted to repairing or maintaining our possessions. "The Harried Leisure Class," we are called by Linder in his book. How true!

From a distance the man who "has everything" may look happy to someone who has much less, or nothing at all, but if you look closely, you may see a life of harried leisure. Are the banquets, cocktail parties, and social blasts of the rich fun? Or are they obligations to be fulfilled? Does high-priced leisure equipment really deliver its promise of happiness? Or does it just get in the way of the relaxed pleasures of a more simple life? Are we—as I am sure we have all secretly suspected for a long time—trapped by the possessions we have worked so hard to buy?

We must find a way out of the leisure fiasco. Nonwork time is being programmed into our lives in ever-increasing amounts, but most people are puzzled and confused. They kill time watching old movies on TV. They busy themselves preparing for future golden days of enjoyment which somehow never seem to come. A friend of mine spent several years of weekends building a forest cabin. When it was finished, he hardly ever went there, because he found that sitting around in the woods doing nothing much wasn't satisfying to him. He didn't want to sell the place and start the building process all over somewhere else, because the dream of an idyllic life in the wilds was part and parcel of the enjoyment of cabin-building. His leisure plans had turned into a cruel joke.

There are things about our way of life which make leisurely leisure hours very difficult. At the risk of oversimplifying slightly, I will say boldly that almost all of our social troubles—not only leisureless leisure but most other dissatisfactions of modern life—stem from our entrapment in a machine-dominated society. Ever since some unknown Asiatic invented the wheel thousands of years ago, we have been avidly pursuing the one best way to accomplish the routine jobs of life. Man has been looking always for the easy way out of both the hard labor and the nit-picking mental tasks.

For many centuries the rate of advancement of machines into our lives was very slow, because science didn't exist to provide the information that technology needed to progress. Gradually, during the Renaissance, the basic physical, chemical, and biological principles of life came into man's view and were put to use in "improving" old-fashioned ways of living. The basic tone of life was changed from a pastoral, manual existence to a machine-dependent one. In the past few hundred years the invasion of technology has become an avalanche. While we used to see an important new machine or technique come into use every twenty years or so, such "advances" are now thrust on us in rapid-fire fashion. The rate of change is immeasurably faster than it was only a few decades ago, and will likely accelerate still more in the future. Already, the human muscle has been replaced almost entirely by the machine, and the technology for replacing the human brain is in the planning stage.

No wonder we are puzzled by our leisure hour frustrations! Everything we do, twenty-four-hours-a-day, is performed in the context of machines and advanced technology. The human value of that technology has hardly been considered at all, ever, by anybody. Industry doesn't build new devices to make people happier. Machines are made to get things done in a "better" way.

Perhaps because we're reconciled to this fact, most people don't expect to be happy while they are working, although they should. As a result, everyone counts even more on the off-hours being the happy ones. Were we to be honest with ourselves about our leisure-time frustrations, we would gain a better understanding of the technological society we live in. If all people did understand how we are being manipulated by technology, maybe, just maybe, we'd have a chance to reconstruct our world and produce more happiness for everyone. But if we don't perceive the role of technology in our dissatisfaction, we'll keep sinking deeper and deeper into the rat-race rut that life has become for many people, rich and poor alike. Most frightening is the realization that increasing technology will make that "rut" seem pleasant. Our future frustrations will be dimmed by tranquilizers or happiness pills. Our human adaptiveness will have erased memories of times when life was more beautiful and will have acclimated us to the ugly environment.

There is only one effective way to save ourselves and future generations. We must rebel against the idea that what matters is the quantity of life, the quantity of wealth, and the quantity of possessions. Quality is what matters. Not gross national product, but the quality of national product. Not total wealth, but happiness. We have gone far along the road of conspicuous consumption and have found that bigger and better worldly goods produce only limited happiness. We have to backtrack and try to find a road that leads to a really enjoyable way of life. I don't mean take a side road. I mean go backwards. Let's stop riding and do some walking. Let's peel potatoes again instead of opening a packet of potato powder. Let's realize that engineering all the little annoyances and chores out of life won't produce happiness and pleasant leisure hours. It will only leave us wondering where the happier times went to and why the present is less pleasant than we thought it would be.

Technology has taken the fun out of leisure because it has liberated us from the need to share work. People used to get together to help each other. I'm not too old to remember the fun of helping a neighboring farmer get in his hay before a summer thunderstorm, then being rewarded with a cool drink of lemonade in his kitchen. Work, yes, but fun, too. Today, we don't have to help each other as much, because technology has made us more self-sufficient. It has given us mechanical slaves, and they are isolating us from our neighbors and friends. Why get together and talk all evening when we can watch television? Why ask a friend what time it is when you can hear the time on the radio? We all listen to the great weatherman of the airwaves instead of arguing among ourselves about the meaning of the configuration of the clouds. No wonder we are frustrated!

In the future—if everyone gets the message—we may become smart enough to equate brains and true human worth with other than material things. We may finally award status on a sensible basis, not to those with fancy clothes and the greatest number of mechanical slaves, but to the person who is least gluttonous of the natural resources on which we all draw for sustenance. The time will soon come when the physical limits of our world are made clear to everyone. If we can all draw the correct meaning from that knowledge, and start sharing more instead of grabbing as much as we can for ourselves, we will get on the right track. Then we'll really start having fun in our spare time, because we will be working together more and getting to know each other better. If most futurists looking at the American lifestyle are right, much of this true leisure will be centered in the home and will contribute mightily to the real income of Americans in the years ahead.

Hidden Wealth in Your Home

When you figure out your personal wealth, you usually start by adding the value of your bank accounts, stocks, bonds, insurance policies, and equity in your home or other real estate, and end up by counting the change in your pocket or purse.

Then you deduct your debts. The mortgage on your home is usually the big one, and you may have other loans as well. What's left after you subtract your total liabilities from your assets indicates very well how much strength and security you have, in a financial sense.

Or does it?

By no means, says Scott Burns in his fascinating book *Home, Inc.* His eye-opening point of view is that the home is a remarkably rich center of wealth and production. And that things and services created in the home have an enormous impact on the quality of our lives. Alvin Toffler makes the same point in his book *The Third Wave*, predicting that the home will play an increasing role as a center of production.

According to Toffler's analysis, the agricultural revolution ended no later than 1750, and the industrial revolution crested around 1955, when white-collar and service workers outnumbered field and factory workers for the first time. Noting that the "second wave" systems are currently in crisis because the era of nonrenewable energy and cheap raw materials is ending, he sees the "third wave" of civilization now beginning as characterized by post-factory methods of production and profound decentralization. By the 1990s, says Toffler, it is likely that telecommunications equipment will be cheaper than commuting, and more and more work will be shifted back to the home.

Right now, of course, home production consists for the most part of the unpaid work people do for themselves. Both Burns and Toffler emphasize that current economic thinking entirely overlooks these activities. The food you grow in your garden and the bread you bake in your kitchen are not counted as part of the gross national product. If you were to buy vegetables and bread, the money gained by the markets supplying them would be tallied as part of our country's economic wealth, though. Homemade clothes, craft projects, personal transportation, and home entertainment are also overlooked.

In the same way, home capital equipment is ignored by economists. When you have your shirts and bedsheets laundered professionally, the equipment used is figured as part of the basic hardware of production in America. Yet your home laundry equipment is forgotten, or considered mere gadgetry.

You can do your laundry at home more cheaply than can a commercial laundry, though, using remarkably efficient home equipment. That's why so many laundries are going out of business, in fact.

I think the ideas of Burns and Toffler are well worth pondering precisely because they throw some light on why conventional economists are unable to say much that's helpful about reviving business and production. All the experts could be barking up the wrong tree. They are trying to understand why money circulates the way it does, while ignoring the important fact that much of our real wealth is not connected to money at all. Any production of goods and services that is not money-related seems not to exist in the eyes of almost all economists.

The market economy—that's what they're interested in. The home is not part of that market economy, except as it represents a center of demand for products and services. But work done and services accomplished in homes are real, even though wages aren't paid. And the productivity of homes is fantastically large.

For example, if you put a money value on all the work done in homes, says Burns, "the total would be equal to the entire amount paid out in wages and salaries by every corporation in the United States." Think of the output that represents! Millions of dresses and other items of clothing! Countless additions and renovations to homes. Probably enough tomatoes and cabbages to circle the globe a dozen times, not to mention all those home-grown ears of corn!

Home production is growing rapidly, too, and could overtake the market economy in total production at some future time. There are important reasons why that's happening.

First, resource shortages are slowing business expansion. Energy, as we all know, is running low. Less well known is the fact that shortages of paper, tin, uranium, and other materials essential to industry will soon limit expansion. Long-range planners for business know about those potential shortages.

Business can decide not to expand, but people must try to create productive homes so that the household economy will expand as the population grows.

Second, many businesses which do expand are doing so "into" the home economy. The do-it-yourself revolution is permeating every dimension of life, even the realm of medical care. People are now administering their own pregnancy tests, taking their own blood pressures and pap smears, and giving themselves many other kinds of tests.

Toys are being made so that final steps of assembly are done in the home. Businesses are turning out a growing number of craft supplies, tools, sewing machines, patterns, how-to books and similar items—all of which increase home production.

Third, growing unemployment in industry, business, and the service field is keeping more people at home, where they are forced to create opportunities for production. And those opportunities are being found—at a remarkable rate. Over half of all the building materials sold are now purchased directly by home-owners.

In Burns's opinion, the market economy has reached its zenith and is being forced by cost factors to transfer some of its traditional work to the home. He wants us to take another look at investments, usually defined in the market economy in terms of hot stocks. His advice: go long on storm windows.

Now and for the future, the homely triple-channel aluminum storm window is probably the best investment any American can make. It offers a tax-free return on investment, three or four times the interest rates on the highest yield bonds, and is likely to offer a better return, over a five-to-ten-year period, than most of the hottest stocks of the sixties.

These are not fanciful claims. About five years ago, the House of Representatives' Ad Hoc Committee on Fuel Conservation announced that the average storm window recovered 13 to 18 percent of its purchase price every year in areas where the winter temperature is 45° Fahrenheit (7° Celsius) or lower. In effect, the storm window buyer is achieving a 30 percent tax-free return on his investment—competitive with Coca-Cola's 28 percent return.

Other statistics show that the home is again becoming a significant center of creative energy. Home centers, numbering approximately five thousand, are growing at a rate of 20 percent a year. The U.S. Department of Commerce has estimated that 80 percent of all paint and 60 percent of all wallpaper is purchased by do-it-yourselfers.

How far should we take this line of thinking? What if you purchased a yogurt maker which cut the cost of homemade yogurt (over store-bought) by 70 percent? What if you filled out your own tax return, repaired your own car, reseated the toilet, insulated your house, cooked most of your meals, and did your own laundry (for a 20 percent savings)? Do these activities represent a contribution to the vitality of the home?

Scott Burns says yes, in that they indicate a movement away from "complete" dependence on the market economy. I think there is value in what he says, although I do not believe that every consumer item purchased necessarily contributes to the hidden wealth in the home. Owning a car would cut down on taxi fares, but owning a bicycle would take the consumer a greater distance from the marketplace.

Whether driven by high inflation and unemployment or not, people appear to have a hunger for personal involvement in "chores" customarily given over to the market economy. Whether this trend demonstrates a desire to save money or to gain the satisfaction of working with the hands, I have no doubt that Americans are becoming more concrete and practical.

Of course, real hidden wealth would be represented by a lifestyle that allowed you to be as free as possible from the conventional economy, a lifestyle that would include gardening, livestock raising, fruit tree culture, timber production, and extensive home food processing and storage.

Homesteading expands garden productivity even more dramatically. Growing fruit trees and keeping small animals on a mini-farm multiply home production capacity. Homesteaders can also grow their own grain for bread, generate some of their power, and produce a surplus of food for sale to neighbors.

Money saved by such enterprises goes further than conventional income because home production is largely tax exempt. You can produce a host of valuable things in your house and garden, and keep all the financial benefits. "Only by moving out of the market economy can labor and capital legitimately avoid taxation," says Burns in *Home, Inc.*

True, as a homeowner you must pay property taxes. But those taxes don't rise as home productivity increases. My guess is that the least productive homes, such as apartments in urban areas, have a greater property tax burden than rural homes surrounded by land. And you can produce far more useful things in a small homestead than you can in an urban apartment.

Wherever you live, though, the pressures of inflation, unemployment, and taxation are helping to change our vision of how we would like to spend our discretionary time. Idleness, which is a lifestyle goal for some Americans, is being seen by more and more as a sure route to boredom and a reduced quality of life.

On the other hand, home productivity leads to psychic as well as physical rewards. Learn to enjoy making something good at home, and you can keep on doing that year after year. You are free to set up your own conditions of work, can decide what you want to make, and even how your products will be used.

True, you will not be at leisure, but your productive activity can be far more satisfying. Even more important, increased home productivity will increase your security. Your own productive capacity is the only real inflation-proof form of capital. As inflation becomes more severe the value of your own production rises too. As long as you create goods and enjoy doing it, you have security against inflation. Generating food and other useful products at home even insulates you against a generalized fraying of the fabric of society. When the world comes apart around you, a good, productive home is the best place to be.

The Coming Conflict over Self-Sufficiency

A good life on little or no money—that's the goal of self-sufficiency. You produce what you need on your own place.

Total self-sufficiency is almost impossible to achieve. Hardly any farmers are self-sufficient, for example. They are too hooked into the money economy. Fuel and machines are needed to run the farm, and those supplies must be purchased, at ever-rising prices. If the economy were to collapse, most farmers would go hungry, because they wouldn't have money to buy the many things they have grown accustomed to using.

Trying to become partially self-sufficient is also a real challenge but is possible. More people than ever are doing it these days in an effort to protect themselves against the erosive effect of inflation.

Another incentive to work for self-sufficiency is growing distrust of the conventional economy and of the whole productive system. "Something bad is likely to happen," more people feel. That bad news could be shortages, such as a food crunch caused by an effective strike of farmers. Or there could be more environmental catastrophes, like the disastrous release of PBBs that contaminated much food produced in Michigan. Fears like that cause people to want to produce more of their own food, and even to stockpile food as protection against shortages.

The drive toward self-sufficiency has been given its greatest push forward by the booming interest in the collection and use of solar energy. Sun energy shines over wide areas. Control of the use of solar energy will probably be very decentralized. Everyone with a place in the sun can participate, including many city people as well as homesteaders and farmers. At this point solar energy is not cheap to collect and use because you must have good devices to make use of it. But at least the coming of the solar age offers promise of putting people more on their own—giving them the chance to be primary producers of energy instead of customers of commercial suppliers.

A suburban or rural homestead that is solar powered, and which can produce food all year long in both an outside garden and a solar greenhouse, begins to make possible a significant amount of self-sufficiency. If the people who live in that homestead also live simply and conserve resources, they can take another long leap toward self-sufficiency. Catch the rays of the sun, produce some of your own food, and shun some of the wasteful ways of the typical American lifestyle, and you'll be well on your way to achieving the goal of personal independence.

Along the way to that dream, though, you'll likely find yourself coping with new challenges and conflicts. Some of the fights stirred up by the self-sufficiency trend will be over access to the resources of personal independence. Other battles will occur between the newly self-sufficient people and those who depend for their bread and butter entirely on the conventional economy. Do some thinking now about these conflicts, and maybe you can counter them effectively.

First, there's the coming challenge to sun rights. Do you own the sun energy that shines onto your property from above? Yes, but only the rays that come straight down, or that cross the property of others to get to your solar collectors. During the winter, when the sun stays low in the sky, solar radiation probably will have to cross a number of property lines to get to your home.

If you live on a south-facing slope you're probably OK. Having a large property helps. But keep in mind that previous legal battles over the shading of resort swimming pools by neighboring high-rise hotels have established the common law principle that the property owner has a right to light from above, but has no guaranteed right to light crossing neighboring property.

People have been making good use of their neighbors' sun for years with few problems, so I think the question of sun rights will be resolved easily for most people. You have to remember, though, that sunlight is now a much more valuable commodity than it used to be. More solar-collecting structures will be built, and some of them will block off sun that used to go to a neighbor. Also, there will be many arguments about big trees that block winter sun. Which is more important—your summer shade or your neighbor's heat in winter? You may try to evade the question, but your shaded neighbor won't. People looking for new homestead sites these days are thinking about sun access before all other factors.

Buying energy and other basic needs from utilities is the total opposite of self-sufficiency. It should not be surprising, therefore, to find that utilities are less than enthusiastic about seeing an age of real self-sufficiency come to pass. They have to oppose self-sufficiency carefully, though, because personal independence is an idea so valued by Americans that direct opposition of utilities to the techniques of self-sufficiency would be extremely bad for their public image.

A few years back, some electric utilities built solar demonstration houses. They were conventional homes, with some solar collectors added. The price tag for the solar option was high, and the cost savings were comparatively low. Those facts were publicized with a very soft-sell. Little or no mention was made of the fact that the efficiency of solar collectors would likely improve and the cost decline. The impact of those demonstrations of solar-power failures on the public's thinking was minimal.

Now the utilities are gearing up for a more direct attack on solar energy. They are upset about the failure of nuclear power to gain wide public acceptance, and want to make sure that solar doesn't move in and take away much of their projected future business. They are doing some hard thinking to come up with antisolar arguments.

Solar power is actually more dangerous than nuclear, Dr. Herbert Inhaber claimed in an article in *The New Scientist*. Dr. Inhaber was formerly scientific adviser to the Atomic Energy Control Board in Ottawa, Ontario. He argues that nuclear power plants are "closely guarded and surrounded by barbed wire," to present minimal risk to the public. Solar collectors, on the other hand, says Inhaber, are perched on thousands of roofs, have no professional guards, and therefore can cause many accidents. He also asserts that the production chain which leads up to the ultimate use of solar energy creates more potential for risk than does the process of building and operating nuclear plants. The many truck drivers delivering solar panels can cause more traffic accidents, for example. Dr. Inhaber uses risk-accounting methods to reach that conclusion.

Such thinking is totally wrong, of course. Nuclear reactors create the potential for disasters so severe that they could change the whole course of human history. The single problem of handling waste products of nuclear reactors is alone sufficient to end their use. Accidents that might be caused by solar-panel use are not at all in the same league. The fact that a scientist linked with nuclear power interests is motivated to make such a comparison is an early warning signal that solar self-sufficiency is viewed as a threat by utility managements.

In this matter and in others, the issue is whether to stay with "the system" or to strike out on your own to improve personal quality of life as promptly as possible. Let's face it. The environment is not pure. Your air, water, and food can be polluted, depending on where and how you live. There are two ways to correct that problem. One is the togetherness way. That involves getting laws passed to stop the pollution of communal resources like air and water. When that happens, everyone enjoys a more healthful environment. A second way is to be self-sufficient and purify your own personal environment.

Surprisingly, opposition is building to the idea of acting individually. The best example is the growing controversy that surrounds water filtering. Numerous city water supplies are known to contain chemicals that can cause cancer in people who drink that water. Many of those chemicals can be removed by passing the water through special filters containing activated carbon, which are not yet in wide use by water companies. The cost of doing that will be rather high, so the public is going to have to support the idea of anticancer water purification if the money is to be spent. Most people drinking that water will have to wait years before the water is cleaned up in central plants.

If you are interested in becoming self-sufficient, you can purify your own water right now, at reasonable cost. You don't have to purify all your water—only that which you drink or use for cooking. You can even build your own filter. The cost of a good home system that should help your family prevent cancer will range from about $15 to well over $200, depending on whether you make or buy the filter.

The Environmental Protection Administration is not enthusiastic about the proliferation of home water-purification systems. Also a very prominent environmental organization once tried to get the EPA to discourage home filtering. Why? Because this group is afraid that if the people who worry about their health purify their own water, they will stop pushing for the purification of everyone's water in central treatment plants. Self-sufficiency in water purification is seen as a threat to the general welfare.

I am totally in favor of home water purification, and I also support improved filtering of water in central plants. My opinion is that more filtering of water by self-sufficient people will accelerate the trend toward central treatment by educating more people to the pressing need to purify water for cancer prevention.

Such conflicts will be plentiful in the years ahead, and economic disturbances also will occur as more people choose to use fewer goods and services in their attempts to disconnect their lives from the declining fortunes of the conventional economy. Nevertheless, the trend toward self-sufficiency is not going to be stopped, or even slowed. It will accelerate.

Two Other Sides
of Self-Sufficiency

It seems to me that increasing antagonism from those still locked completely into the buy-and-sell economy will help speed the movement toward self-sufficiency by bringing the issue forward for discussion. (Too many people don't yet even *think* about greater personal independence.)

But if this is so, what *is* holding back the separation of people from the money economy? Quite probably it is too narrow a view of what self-sufficiency is. Even enlightened and highly motivated people see it only as the effort to produce things for their personal or family use. Solar panels of the roof capture energy. A large garden produces enough food to last through a whole winter. Those are considered acts of self-sufficient living.

There is far more to self-sufficiency (or at least the trend in that direction) than producing things yourself, though. There are two other very important things which must be done before personal independence becomes even remotely possible.

Conservation is vital. Real self-sufficiency can be achieved only in societies where people use far smaller amounts of fuel than do Americans. They also eat less, which is extremely important. (It has been estimated that 20 percent of all adults in the United States are overweight to a degree that may interfere with their health.)

People are beginning to insulate their homes and drive smaller cars, but Americans still have a long way to go in conservation before they can get their input needs within reach of efforts at self-sufficiency. My guess is that we'll never become as frugal as the Chinese or people in peasant cultures, but I'm sure there's little hope of real self-sufficiency here until we cut way back on our fuel and food inputs. Note that I said inputs, not imports.

Waste control is the second aspect of self-sufficiency, and it is every bit as important as production and conservation. No matter how frugally people live, they will always produce some waste products. In a self-sufficient society, those wastes are both kept to a minimum and are used as raw materials for further production. In a self-sufficient household or homestead there is a constant recycling from waste to useful product and back to waste again. Not only is there no hope of self-sufficiency if you don't use your wastes, but by definition you aren't self-sufficient if you have to dump bad stuff on other people in order to live.

I feel that people can learn the most about self-sufficiency by studying their own wastes. For one thing, you can use your production of wastes as a gauge to measure your progress toward conservation. Recycle everything you can, in particular paper, bottles, and cans. Then try to put a limit on the number of cans or other wastes you produce that require carrying off to a dump or incinerator somewhere. It would not be out of order even to keep a log of the number of trash bags or cans you fill each month. Aim to keep cutting back the number as you become more careful in your purchases.

Again, China comes to mind. When I was there I saw that trash does not exist, at least in the sense we use that word. The primary reason is that the things which become trash here are produced in China in extremely limited quantities. There are very few Styrofoam packages, corrugated cartons, plastic soap bottles, and certainly no beer cans. Shipping containers which are no longer needed are put to some other use. I'm not saying we should stop the manufacture of potential trash entirely, but certainly we could cut back and reuse things more without suffering. We will probably be forced to do that soon anyway.

Enlightened water management in the home is crucial to efforts at self-sufficiency. A large proportion of our household waste is liquid. Most of that is water used for washing and sewage disposal. We use far more water than we really need, and that not only creates potential shortages but also costs us money for pumping and sewage disposal. Maybe we don't pay the bills directly, but we do so indirectly when we pay water fees and taxes that cover sewage-treatment costs.

A major problem in achieving self-sufficiency is that modern home technology mixes human wastes with water so that those wastes can be carried off easily to a distant sewage-treatment plant. We now know that that isn't logical, because the cost of separating the solid from the liquid is exorbitant. Also, the separation can't be accomplished completely, so the water released from the sewage plant into rivers, lakes, and the ocean is rich with nitrogen, phosphates, and other nutrients that would be very useful for growing plants.

Early steps have been made to rectify that problem, in particular the building of composting or dry toilets like the Clivus Multrum. But we need more improved models that don't smell and allow the easy mixing of human wastes with table scraps to produce a useful compost.

I think such toilets can eventually be worked out and used by many people. In particular, I think we need a new approach to recovering the nutrients in urine. There is basically no potential health hazard in using urine as a fertilizer as long as the person from whom it was taken is healthy. And flushing a five-gallon toilet each time a member of the family urinates is extremely wasteful. A separate urine toilet, which could provide for nutrient recovery, would be especially helpful for people using septic tanks in areas with poor soil percolation. Why try to get five gallons of water to soak into the soil when you are trying to manage only a few ounces of usually sterile liquid?

What we really need to do is to learn to mix our wastes in the proper way so that the ingredients complement each other and a healthful, useful product emerges. Such mixing of complementary wastes is the rationale behind composting and is exactly why it has proven to be such a useful method.

The range of wastes produced by the average home is wide. From the yard we get grass clippings, leaves, twigs, weeds, and stalks of flowers and vegetable plants. From the house come table scraps and other garbage, as well as wood ashes. The human and animal occupants of the house produce wastes which are now beginning to be composted on site in certain carefully designed units like the Clivus Multrum and other dry toilets.

No approach toward self-sufficiency can be made without the proper mixing of such household and yard organic wastes in a compost system. There are two reasons why that is essential. First, we can't rely on others to handle our wastes and feel self-sufficient. Second and more important, we need the nutrients that are in those wastes to fertilize our gardens. Unless we continually utilize nutrients, instead of having them carted off to some dump or river, we are breaking the link in the cycle of life which is at the core of self-sufficiency.

Gardens of the Future

Trying to predict the future is usually an exercise in futility. A prediction can be thwarted in so many ways, by events that are totally unpredictable. Yet somehow I have the feeling that visualizing now the gardens of tomorrow is not a difficult thing to do. We know that our society is already locked into a process of rapid change, and we also know the general nature of that "lock" and can easily imagine what it will require us to do.

Population increases continue, and escalating food costs and possible shortages are in the offing—partly because both California and Florida, major sources of winter produce, are losing farmland to housing and other development at a rapid rate. Those states will someday cease being able to send food to people in the rest of the country. The price of commercial food also will be driven up by the higher costs of chemicals. Nitrogen fertilizer production is heavily dependent on the use of natural gas, a fuel which is likely to experience dramatic cost increases. Similar price hikes will hit phosphorus and potash, which are important fertilizers.

As a result of these pressures and changes, there will be more gardens in the future, for the time is coming when once again we'll have to garden to get the food we need, just as our great-grandparents did. But new intensive, labor-saving methods will make that task much easier. And I believe there will be a continuous flow of new plants, techniques, and ideas that will make gardening far more productive and rewarding in years to come.

The nature of home itself will change. Greenhouses, heated largely by energy from the sun, will be common. In fact, I feel that the greenhouse will be a part of the heating system of many homes. There are many advantages to linking living space to a solar-heated greenhouse. Heat captured by the greenhouse during the day can be circulated into the house, and carbon dioxide exhaled by people living in the house will be vented into the greenhouse, where it will help the growth of plants. One of the most efficient and inexpensive collectors of solar energy, the double- or triple-walled plastic-insulated greenhouse, is also an essential tool, making possible year-round food production in decentralized communities. They are already springing up like mushrooms in some areas, and you'll be seeing them all over soon. To help in heat storage, many of these greenhouses will have fish ponds. Which leads me right into another prediction: home aquaculture will be commonplace.

As meat becomes ever more expensive and ocean fish catches decline, people will find it natural to grow some of this excellent food themselves. Some of the best kinds of fish for pond culture are still largely unknown to consumers. Tilapia, an African fish mentioned in the Bible, is thought to be one of the most promising. It tastes good, reproduces easily, and eats largely inexpensive plant foods. Some types of carp also hold similar promise. Tilapia and carp may not sound like glamour foods, but I think you'll be hearing more about them in the future, and perhaps raising them, too.

Trout and catfish are already big in the aquaculture scene, and both offer important nutritional advantages over such American dinner staples as beef and pork. Catfish is very popular in the South and Midwest right now and eventually could become widely grown in other regions, too. Even in a small greenhouse pond, such fish can be stocked at a high rate. That's because these highly efficient converters of feed to flesh can "stand" one on top of another as well as side-by-side, as land animals do.

To make home aquaculture even more efficient and economical, table scraps will be shredded and fed to fish, which in turn will be important sources of animal protein for the family. We are already recycling kitchen wastes in this way at the Organic Gardening and Farming Research Center, and I see no reason why the technique should not become widely used well before the end of this century.

Water from the home fish pond will become an important source of fertility for the garden. The "droppings" of fish are extremely rich in nutrients and help gardens produce better. No better irrigation water can be found anywhere.

The house I see in our future will help gardening in other important ways. A cool, humidified, insulated room will be provided for storage of winter vegetables and root crops—just the way that used to be done years ago. We will be forced by economic and resource pressures to go back to the root cellar idea. But perhaps more important, the future home will provide room and equipment for drying, cleaning, canning, and other food processing chores. The modern American homemaker has already started moving away from additive-laden convenience foods and back to basic food ingredients. That momentum will continue, and in twenty years we will see people doing a wide variety of basic food preparation tasks in their homes. Even slaughtering of small animals in the home will be commonplace, as it was only a few decades ago.

I predict that much less area will be used for lawns in twenty years. Lawns tend to be expensive, and people are tempted to fertilize them with nutrients that would be better applied to food gardens. But the main reason that lawns will be downgraded is that the homestead of the future will spread out and require more space.

First of all, the home greenhouse will take a slice of lawn area. So will the garden itself, which I think will be much larger. Solar collectors can be placed on what is now lawn.

The more functional yard of the future will also be used for game courts, shelters for small animals, compost heaps, fish ponds, and other facilities of food-production importance.

There will be important changes in the kinds of ornamental

plants people use in and around lawn areas. Trees and shrubs can be good sources of food as well as valuable ornamentals, and people are bound to discover that planting handsome fruit, nut, or pod-bearing plants makes good sense. A few of the edible-fruiting ornamentals likely to become more popular are the American elderberry, black mulberry, common pawpaw and persimmon, Juneberry, loquat, rugosa rose, smooth gooseberry, and Western sand cherry. Tomorrow's suburban homestead might also feature nut trees such as the Allegheny chinquapin, Chinese chestnut, and pinyon pine, or pod-bearers like the carob, common honey locust, and mesquite.

The greater food processing and storage capacity that homes of the future will have also will change the nature of the plants that they grow. I am at a loss to predict with any certainty what those plants will be. Tastes and fashions in food change. Even more significant, no one knows for sure what the plant breeders are up to. Recently, for example, they developed an edible-podded pea that is far superior in taste and ease of growing to older peas. It could revolutionize pea growing by making the shelling of peas unnecessary and probably will cause people to devote much more space to that tasty and nutritious vegetable.

New harvesting equipment could make the growing of dry staples like beans more popular and could simplify the digging of root crops. Rodale researchers are delving into both these areas, but others are working on them, too. The National Center for Appropriate Technology in Butte, Montana, is funded by the Community Services Administration as part of its Emergency Energy Conservation Services Program. Its researchers are working on developing technologies applicable to the energy-related needs of low-income people and communities. The main thrust of their effort will be to try to unlock lower-income people from the viselike grip of rising costs for food, energy, and other needs by developing new techniques for home production.

The highly productive home gardens of tomorrow will, I think, be the sprouts from which many new small farms will grow. The small-scale farmers of the future can hardly learn their craft in the land-grant colleges, which preach bigness in almost every way. These new farmers will start as gardeners and grow from there. I think also that we will see the size of gardens increase, so that the distinction between a large garden and a small farm will become blurred.

The new wave of small farms will fill in the chinks of land made available as some of the old-style farmers are driven out of business by ever-bigger farming conglomerates. I think there is room now for many more small farms of the future. Much land that could be used to grow vegetables, beans, specialty crops, and fruit is lying idle. Those acres growing up to weeds might be made into profitable farms if the proper plants and cropping systems for efficient small farms are developed by researchers.

I suspect that people displaced by the trend to consolidate farms into ever-larger units, as well as those who don't want to fit into city life, will return to the land and make these small spaces productive. Large farms today aren't suited to produce the fresh, natural foods that are in growing demand. They will be even less suited for that task in the future, as agribusiness turns more and more to the manufacture of semisynthetic foods from bulk commodities like soybeans, cornstarch, and even petroleum.

The garden-farms that are a growing part of our food future have another important value. They can be operated as closed systems. Organic wastes of both the community and the farm itself can be collected, composted, and returned to the land. By doing that, the vitally important minerals and nitrogen in those wastes can be preserved and used over and over again.

The recycling of minerals in that way is more than just a step toward greater commercial and ecological efficiency. It is a significant movement toward the creation of a permanent human society on this planet. Our present system of production is in reality a bleeding process in which the riches of the earth are drained away to create the things we need to support ourselves. As long as we allow that bleeding to continue, we are imposing on ourselves a time-limit for survival.

There need not be a limit to our tenure. We can learn to live happily, producing all the food and other goods we need, without wasting the resources that are going to be needed by future generations. There, in the concept of the creation of a sustainable way of life, is our next frontier.

Index

A

Administration on Aging, 195
Agricultural Research, 83
Agro-Ecosystems, 30
Airborne hormones, from
    insects, 33
Air pollution
    indicated by plants, 19
    measured by tobacco
        growth, 19
Algae, 18
Amaranth, 132
American diet, 84
American Dust Bowl, 13, 16
Animal fats, 92–96
Annals of Internal Medicine,
    126
Antibiotics, as medication, 165
Anticancer program, 111–12
Azotobacter, 26, 211

B

Bacillus thuringiensis, 32
Bacteria, in bottled water, 140
Basic food groups, 105–6
*Biological Control of Insect
    Pests and Weeds*, 32
Biological control of insects,
    31, 34
Birth control, for population, 2
Blight, effect on crops, 27
Blood pressure, 179–85
    diastolic measurement,
        179
    high, causes of, 180
    how to read, 179
    ideal range, 179
    range for children, 181
    and renin, 180–82
    sphygmomanometer, for
        measurement, 183–84